"Tightly-written by Max Allan Collins and drawn in the spare, Johnny Craig style by Terry Beatty."
THE COMIC READER

"Engagingly understated...EXTREMELY well done..."
FANTASY ADVERTISER

"The hardest thing to do well in comics...and they have brought it off."
COMICS BUYER'S GUIDE

PRINTED IN CANADA

The Files of Ms. TREE

by Max Collins and Terry Beatty

Aardvark-Vanaheim Inc.   *Volume One*

Denise Loubert, publisher

First Printing: Summer 1984

Printed in Canada

ISBN 0-919359-05-1

I, FOR AN EYE

introduction by Max Collins

Has it really been three years since Terry Beatty and I began working on MS. TREE? Somehow, it seems like yesterday; and, somehow, it seems like it took place an incarnation or two ago...

Re-reading the original six-part ECLIPSE MAGAZINE serial, I'm pleased to see (he said modestly) that the old girl holds up pretty well. That the work was done over a rather long period of time - a year - tends to make apparent certain shifts in the approach to the writing and, perhaps more overtly, the artwork. The former reflects me getting used to the less restrictive medium of the comic book page (as opposed to the daily and Sunday comic strip). The latter reflects, I think, the interesting tension that exists in Terry Beatty's work, between his instinct to be "cartoony" and the increasing needs of this particular strip to be drawn rather more realistically.

Let me backtrack a bit, and relate some personal history to those of you who haven't read the several interviews we've given about MS. TREE (to such magazines as COMICS SCENE, COMICS COLLECTOR, COMICS FEATURE and, yes, even THE COMICS JOURNAL). I've also ruminated publicly on this subject on the letters page of the MS. TREE monthly comic book, and in radio and television interviews, so any readers who've heard all this before are cordially invited to skim till something new turns up. And some new, previously unrevealed things will turn up, that much I can promise you...

Both Terry Beatty and I are life residents of Muscatine, Iowa, a town of 25,000 or so on the polluted banks of the muddy Mississippi. But enough about Terry.

My interest in comic strips and fictional detectives harks back to the same moment: the day my mother (little did she know) put in my hot little six-year old hands a tome filled with blood, thunder, villainy and detection: a DICK TRACY comic book. Via the covers of those first several DICK TRACY comics my impressionable young mind was exposed to vivid color depictions of bullets flying through various bad-guy brains, much as the peculiarly grotesque and yet strangely human world of Chester Gould went crashing through my own brain, spiraling through my preadolescent sensibilities, a virtual four-color slug. I was, quite obviously, never the same again.

For years I stayed cooped up in my room (emerging occasionally for meals and television and, when the issue was pressed, school), writing and drawing my own comics. For three years I did something called "Ghost of the Law," which was a home-made strip a lot like THE SPIRIT, only I hadn't yet heard of THE SPIRIT (also, of course, my drawing fell slightly short of Will Eisner's). By the time I hit junior high school, I was also hit by any number of unsympathetic art teachers, all of whom felt I was "wasting" my talent, none of whom managed to discourage me from my all-consuming notion of being a cartoonist when I grew up.

Then three men took me in an alley and beat that notion out of me: their names were not Moe, Larry and Curly, or even Shemp. (Or Joe Besser, either). They were three untrustworthy thugs name of Hammett, Chandler and Spillane.

The tough-and-tender works of these three men also went spiraling through my brain, like a pulpwood bullet this time, and by the ninth grade I was no longer cartooning; my artwork was limited to sketching preliminary cover art for the paperbacks I aimed to write and sell. A sympathetic English teacher at West Junior High gave me my first chance at putting my work in front of the public: I remember vividly reading my "Matt Savage" private eye story (called "The Girl in the River") to a class quite astounded that their teacher was allowing them to be read such racy, violent stuff, written by one of their own, no less. Through high school, having my friends read my manuscripts (and like them) was encouraging, since the publishers I was sending the books to weren't buying.

During my sophomore year in high school, my parents drove me into Chicago, where I delivered a manuscript to a notorious latterday pulp house called Novel Books - they published rather traditional tough-guy novels with a little sex tossed in and foisted off on an unsuspecting public as dirty books (you'd be surprised what passed for pornography in 1964). The editor there, one Tony Licata, was shocked to find that the author of the Matt Savage novels he'd been encouragingly rejecting was fourteen years old. He was impressed, I think. Not enough to buy one of the books, however....

Somehow I managed not to give up, even at the University of Iowa's Writers Workshop where certain teachers and students looked down their noses at what I was up to. This all changed when I sold the first novel in my Nolan series, BAIT MONEY, just before I graduated. Suddenly teachers were claiming me as theirs, and my fellow students were wondering if I would mention their names to my agent. For the record, the instructor at Iowa City who was most helpful to me, who in fact landed me an agent in addition to teaching me much about this here thing us writers like to call prose was an hombre name of Richard Yates - one of the finest serious novelists America has ever produced, by the way.

Let me pause to put the world in context. By "the world," I mean the world around me as I was writing my tough-guy novels out of my bedroom in my parents' home in Muscatine, Iowa. I began seriously trying to sell my work (through the mail, like THE WRITER'S DIGEST said) in 1962. The first novel sold in 1971. That's a span of nine years - during which things changed; various Kennedys got assassinated, the war in Vietnam grew, the war in Vietnam grew unpopular (fortunately), rock 'n' roll turned into an art form (unfortunately), hair got longer, some of us took drugs, some of us took too **many** drugs (a few of us didn't), a lot of us thought we got our consciousnesses raised, and peace and love were here to stay, man. Things changed. In 1964 I was thinking Barry Goldwater would make a nifty President; in 1969 I was thinking about moving to Canada (and finally did, in a way, didn't I?).

Throughout these turbulent times, the subject matter of my writing remained "tough-guy" - although I had discovered a number of writers in that field who, unlike Hammett, Chandler and Spillane, did not primarily write about private eyes or cops. These included James M. Cain, Jim Thompson, Horace McCoy, W.R. Burnett, Donald E. Westlake and Richard Stark. A day that came to shape my professional writing career was when I discovered that Westlake (who wrote light-hearted crime novels in a manner that seemed to combine elements of Damon Runyon and Neil Simon) and Stark (who wrote cold, deadly crime novels in a manner that combined Dashiell Hammett and W.R. Burnett) were the same writer. Oddly enough, I'd had the books of Westlake and those of his pseudonymous other self Stark next to each other on my shelf, with a divider between them; I removed the divider, and sat there and thought about how writers don't need to limit themselves, even when working within a genre.

Anyway, private eyes began to seem out-of-date to me; they seemed something that belonged to the 30's (Hammett), '40s (Chandler) and '50s (Spillane). Latterday private eye novels either struck me as hollow pastiches or pretentious literary exercises. Even Ross MacDonald - who falls into that second category - didn't appeal to me, although I acknowledged him the best of his kind.

And the times around me (the Chicago Democratic Convention and Kent State, for instance) made me less than eager to write about a cop hero, even a private one.

So I turned to crime, and my initial novels (the Nolan series, the Quarry series) concerned, respectively, a professional thief and a hitman. I felt their amorality reflected the period in which they were written; I still do. I did a couple of books about a character called Mallory, a mystery writer in a small town in Iowa (where **do** you get your ideas?) that took me back into private-eye territory, but only the outskirts.

I've recounted elsewhere the story of the abortive comic strip HEAVEN AND HELLER, but I should mention it again here, because it represents my first professional encounter with (a) comic strips, and (2) private eyes. Also - attention, skimmers - I am about to reveal the truth behind the origin of MS. TREE. Around 1975 a friend of mine I'd met in original comic-art collecting moved from the East Coast to Geneva, Illinois - relatively close to me. Closer than the East Coast, anyway. His name was (and is) Rick Marschall, and he had an interesting job: comics editor for Field Enterprises. He also had an interesting notion: that I create a comic strip for him. A continuity.

Rick felt it was time that a story strip be launched in a more adult mode; in the wake of DOONESBURY, it was suggested that such words as "hell" and "damn" might be permissable, and storylines might explore such topics as alcoholism, race prejudice and sexual infidelity. He also felt that the setting ought to be the '30s, partially because of the wave of nostalgia that had hit the country in recent years, partially because it would tie our new strip to the Golden Age of the comic strip continuity.

I came up with a tough detective called Nate Heller, wrote a continuity set in Chicago in the '30s, and Rick and I spent hour upon hour in his Lake Geneva home brainstorming, planning just how to launch the strip, discussing possible artists, kicking around promotional gimmicks and story gambits.

One gambit that I came up with, which Rick immediately embraced, was to unexpectedly kill off one of the title characters. The strip was to be called HEAVEN AND HELLER, and Heller's girl friend, Heaven - set up from the beginning as a major and presumably recurring character (name in the title, after all!) - would die just after the first continuity, shortly after becoming Heller's secretary. Heller would, of course, seek revenge, and thereafter be haunted by her memory. We thought it would cause a big sensation, and decided that once this strip had set the comics world on its ear, a follow-up strip would have to be launched. I said, "Let's do a sex reversal of HELLER - we'll have the private eye get murdered, and the secretary/lover take over his agency - and her first case will be to solve his murder!" Rick applauded that notion, but we got back to the immediate business at hand: HEAVEN AND HELLER.

To put this story out of its misery, I'll say only that after some lovely samples were put together by the great Ray Gotto (of OZARK IKE fame), HEAVEN AND HELLER went into limbo - because Rick left his position at Field, at which time all his current projects were shelved. Rick, over the next several years, tried to market the strip to other syndicates; we even (at the request of King Features) had a second, beautiful batch of samples worked up by Fred DaSilva (currently the REX MORGAN MD artist). Close but no cigar (or is that Segar?). I went back to book-writing, figuring this brief excursion into comics was a fluke - a fun, memorable fluke, but a fluke.

By 1977, the '60s receding in the distance like a drug-induced delusion, I was comfortably settled in a home of my own, happily married to my childhood sweetheart Barb, my writing career humming along unspectacularly, but humming along. I'd just resigned from a teaching position at the local community college, having grown bored of explaining what a comma splice is to uncomprehending ears, and was in the midst of working with a successful regional rock group, CRUSIN', in which I sang and played keyboards. We'd just built a studio and were planning to record. Then the phone rang.

It was Don Michel, Vice President and Editor of the Chicago Tribune/New York News Syndicate. He informed me that Chester Gould was about to retire. And he wondered if I might be interested in trying out for DICK TRACY?

It seems the powers-that-be at the Tribune Syndicate came up with the notion that a mystery writer (rather than a comics pro) would be an interesting candidate to take over the scripting of the comic strip about America's most famous fictional detective. They had called around and asked various people in the business if they knew of anyone who might be appropriate to this task; my name came up

several times - among the people the Syndicate called were Rick Marschall (who told them about HEAVEN AND HELLER) and my then-agent, Knox Burger. Somebody - to this day I don't know who - called to their attention the fact that the novels in my Nolan series were chockful of comics references, Nolan's sidekick Jon being a comic-book fan and would-be cartoonist.

So I was given a chance to write a synopsis, and I did - I wrote the first Angeltop story, overnight, and sent it off to them Special Delivery. A week later, Don Michel and Tribune Syndicate President Bob Reed flew to Chicago, where we met, and they interviewed me and offered me a contract.

I had never intended to write comics. Comics had remained my hobby - they were virgin territory, one area in the arts that I could truly enjoy, never having gotten my feet wet professionally in their pond (**not** a metaphor Chandler would have been proud of, incidentally). As a writer of fiction, I had lost much of my joy for reading fiction; I could only read a novel or short story from the perspective of a "guy in the business" - I couldn't seem to turn off my critical/professional facilities and just enjoy the damn thing. I'd had the same experience with rock 'n' roll. And now comics were being taken away from me as a hobby.

On the other hand, they were being given to me as a livelihood, so what the hell.

I worked on DICK TRACY with Rick Fletcher, a terrific, vastly underrated artist who had been Chester Gould's assistant for sixteen years before joining me to produce the strip independently of Chet (despite Gould's sharing our byline in the early years, he had no part in any of the strip's production other than some very general consulting with me, by phone, early on). Unfortunately, Rick and I had a somewhat rocky professional association; there was a gulf between us having to do with years and miles and Rick's mistaken assumption that he would take over the strip **alone**, as artist **and** writer. I'm afraid I was, to Rick, simply that damn writer he'd been stuck with by the Syndicate. We rarely had "words" - but our friendship was polite at best; and we never had what should come out of any good collaboration - synergy. Two plus two equals five. We lacked the give-and-take - despite concerted efforts on my part - necessary to make a partnership truly sing. (By the way, my current TRACY partnership, with Dick Locher, the acclaimed editorial cartoonist who had preceded Rick as Chet Gould's assistant, is singing along quite nicely, thank you.)

I'm proud of the work Rick and I produced; I think it speaks well of our respective talents that it hit a rather consistently high mark - despite the fact that it was produced under an "I do the art, you do the writing" sort of collaboration.

During the Fletcher years, I found myself enjoying doing comics, but yearning for the experience of a more synergetic collaboration.

For some time I'd been keeping an eye on the developing artistic talent of a young friend of mine, Terry Beatty. He'd introduced himself to me at Happy Joe's, a pizza and ice cream parlor in Muscatine, probably around 1973; he must've been about fifteen at the time. He let me know how much he liked my books, BAIT MONEY and BLOOD MONEY. He then explained that he was the son of Ernest Beatty, my English teacher back in junior high - the very one who'd let my read my blood-and-thunder short stories to the class.

Over the following years, Terry and I discovered we had similar interests - we seemed to like the same comics and movies and mystery novels and rock 'n' roll - and I patiently waited for him to mature into somebody I could be seen in public with. Finally, I gave up on waiting for that to happen and just started being seen in public with him, anyway, never looking back.

Fairly early on I discovered Terry was doing very primitive, cartoony, underground-influenced art for a high school humor magazine. There was a real spark in the work - imagination, talent, even originality. Terry went on to be a disc jockey for a local FM station, while still in high school, and somehow or other that led to him becoming sound man/roadie for my rock band.

This meant Terry was on the sidelines during the creation of HEAVEN AND HELLER and my landing of the DICK TRACY assignment, and unspoken between us was the understanding that, when Terry got "good enough," we would work together. My increasing frustration with the lack of give-and-take on my TRACY collaboration led me, finally, to suggest that Terry and I work up ANNIE samples for the Tribune Syndicate. This was, I believe, in 1978. The ANNIE strip was then in Harold Gray reruns, appearing in only a handful of papers, and seemed moribund; but the Broadway show was such a media smash, I figured we had a shot at selling a revived ANNIE.

I had a meeting in Chicago with Don Michel and Rick Fletcher (ironically, one of several ill-fated attempts to loosen up the working arrangement between Rick and me) and, after Rick departed, I asked Don if I could show him something - an ANNIE sample Sunday.

Don immediately liked the page, admitted the Syndicate had had a revival of ANNIE in development, and that they'd requested several samples from big-name cartoonists, none of whom (he said) had come up with anything as good as this. He met Terry, and we discussed possible plans for the strip. Within a week, I'd been commissioned by the Syndicate to develop the synopsis of the first ANNIE story, with the understanding that upon approval Terry and I would turn it into strips. In a few weeks the synopsis was approved, and Terry and I were commissioned to do the first two weeks.

Time slogged by, and somewhere along the line, the Syndicate changed its mind. I was told that Terry's youth and lack of experience and credentials worried them, although they felt the work showed promise. Finally I was offered the chance to write the strip, for an artist they would provide. I said no. I'd been down that road before. A few months later Len Starr emerged as ANNIE's new poppa, and has done a splendid job.

(Don Michel later commissioned Terry and me to work on several other projects-in-development for the Tribune Syndicate, including asking us to work up a rock 'n' roll strip, which we did - a modernized HAROLD TEEN we called CAROL TEEN; that, too, failed to get off the Syndicate's back burner. Their current ELWOOD is, I think, what the notion of a rock 'n' roll strip ended up being.)

The best way of dealing with the disappointment of ANNIE, I thought, was to launch a new project. So Terry and I began producing a self-contained tabloid page of comics - six features of varying types, mostly humor - which we syndicated to weekly newspapers (including "shoppers") around the country; we were a modest success, with about sixteen papers including the Chicago READER (who used only our minute mystery feature, MIKE MIST). But after a year we folded up THE COMICS PAGE and began working on other projects (the above-mentioned CAROL TEEN among them).

Dean Mullaney, whose Eclipse Enterprises had just published the graphic novel DETECTIVES, INC., met us at the 1980 Chicago comics con. It turned out he was a big TRACY fan, and had seen MIKE MIST in the Chicago READER; we discussed the possibility of Eclipse doing a MIST collection, which they soon did (Dean would be glad to sell you one).

Not long after, Dean called - and as it happened, Terry was at my house watching an old movie on TV - and wondered if Terry and I might like to work up something for this new book he was putting together - ECLIPSE MAGAZINE. **Maybe a private eye strip,** he said. **Do you have any ideas?**

From out of the deep, dark, dank recesses of my brain I dredged the HEAVEN AND HELLER sex-reversal idea: the secretary marries the private eye and, on their wedding night, the private eye is killed, bequeathing her the business and his unsolved murder. Mike Hammer finally marries Velda, only to be killed and she has to fill his shoes - and holster.

Terrific! Dean said. **Do you have a name for the feature?**

Sure, I said, thinking quickly, my DICK TRACY-twisted brain searching for a fast pun; **how 'bout...MS. TREE?**

So, after all those years, I was finally writing a full-fledged private-eye yarn. (I was also fooling with the notion of doing HELLER as a novel...but that's another story) (called TRUE DETECTIVE, St. Martin's Press, $14.95).

Immediately we rejected certain cliches - the whiskey bottle in the bottom desk drawer, the trenchcoat, the gloomy self-consciously existential narration, all the trappings that seemed to me to be the makings of pastiche and unintentional parody. There would be a film **noir** atmosphere - but we'd put Ms. Tree in a modern setting, a modern suite of offices, not some rundown building out of a '40s movie. Having a woman as hero was a good first step away from the norm - but we determined not to make her a super-woman; she wouldn't be master of eighteen martial arts - she'd just have a gun.

Also, Terry and I had been bitching back and forth for months about the increasingly incoherent comic books that were being fobbed off on an idiotically receptive public. Didn't anybody remember how comics were supposed to work? The size, the shape of the frame, had become more important than what went in it. We kept coming back to a mutual favorite - Johnny Craig of EC fame - whose clean, straightforward artwork complimented his own terse, quietly evocative writing. We consciously set out to produce what I've termed elsewhere "an experiment in coherence." I also wanted the writing to be lean, efficient, in response to the increasingly wordy nonsense many comic-book writers were indulging in, and the pompous artiness of many modern-day private-eye novelists. The writing style in MS. TREE has as its most conscious sources the Continental Op short stories of Dashiell Hammett and Jack Webb's DRAGNET (particularly the radio version).

MS. TREE (and the Collins/Beatty collaboration) has evolved since this first story. I notice the language here is rather more profane than is our current bent; when we moved to a color comic book, with MS. TREE'S THRILLING DETECTIVE ADVENTURES #1, I pulled back on that score - assuming that our $1 color audience might include younger readers than the $2.95 black-and-white audience of ECLIPSE MAGAZINE. I have not come to regret

that decision - the use of profanity in the word balloons of I, FOR AN EYE strikes me as a little harsh, even jarring, especially in the context of Terry's early, unabashedly cartoony drawing. It's perhaps interesting to note that the right balance has been achieved on MS. TREE only as I've pulled back somewhat on the profane dialogue and Terry has moved forward into more illustrational, "realistic" drawing.

I find Terry's drawing, here, bold, strong and, well, charming. He's much better than this, now; but, in a sense, he may never draw as well again. The youthful enthusiasm of a young cartoonist - one whose natural leaning is to humorous cartooning by the way - setting out to do his first professional comic book story is exhilarating, I think. While I write a full, detailed script, Terry Beatty's own touches are everywhere - for example, he chose to portray in the background at the cemetery a statue of an angel with a broken arm - the perfect metaphorical image of Ms. Tree; he aptly chose to pose Ms. Tree against a jagged, explosive abstract painting during the final confrontation scene. Those who found the early MS. TREE lacking (and with one notable exception our critics were generally kind) might have taken into consideration that this was indeed Terry Beatty's first professional comic book work; and the first comic book story I had ever written, either. (DICK TRACY is comics, yes, but the comic strip form and the comic-book - or, if you will, "graphic story" - form are quite different).

Perhaps I should comment on the various in jokes and references in this first story. To pay homage to the primary source of MS. TREE - Mickey Spillane's Mike Hammer (and Hammer's secretary Velda) - Mike Tree physically is patterned upon Mike Hammer as portrayed in the late Ed Robbins' classic early '50s comic strip interpretation of the character. Jack Webb and DRAGNET are paid tribute, as well (see if you can figure out who Ms. Tree's father is). Several of the chapter titles echo mystery novels that Terry and I admire: KISS TOMORROW HELLO is a twist (albeit obvious) on Horace McCoy's KISS TOMORROW GOODBYE; one of our favorite private-eye writers is the underrated, almost unknown Mike Roscoe - whose ONE TEAR FOR MY GRAVE is echoed by our ONE GRAVE FOR MY TEARS, and our DEATH IS A LITTLE BLACK BOOK derives from his DEATH IS A ROUND BLACK BALL.

I would like to thank two people: our former publisher Dean Mullaney, who believed in MS. TREE and Collins and Beatty; and our current publisher, Deni Sim, who agrees with us that the serialized MS. TREE stories should be collected in volumes like...well, like this.

Finally, I must admit that I have gotten from

MS. TREE what I hoped to get - which is to say, more out of it than I put in. Working with a talented young artist in my own home town has allowed me to watch (and make suggestions along the way) as the story begins as roughs and then comes to life in finished pencils and at last takes on the sheen of inks. I have indeed seen two and two add up to five.
   Sometimes six.

Max Allan Collins
April 13, 1984

THE FIRST OFFICIAL MS. TREE DRAWING. DONE IN 1980.

I, FOR AN EYE

Ms. TREE

"I, FOR AN EYE"
by Max Collins & Terry Beatty

Chapter One — THE GIRL IN THE RED WEDDING DRESS

© 1981 by Collins and Beatty

TODAY WAS OUR WEDDING DAY... TONIGHT OUR HONEYMOON... TOMORROW... TOMORROW...

1

THIS MORNING IN THE CITY, IT DIDN'T LOOK LIKE RAIN...

A LITTLE COLD, MAYBE, FOR A BRIGHT SPRING MORNING— BUT JUST RIGHT TO WAKE THE WORK FORCE—

I HAD TO WORK ON THE MORNING OF MY WEDDING DAY— THE BOSS INSISTED.

IF HE SOUNDS MEAN, WELL, I WON'T DENY IT— BUT "TOUGH" WOULD BE A BETTER WORD.

Tree Investigations Inc.

YOU MAY BE WONDERING WHAT KIND OF OGRE WOULD MAKE A GIRL WORK ON HER WEDDING DAY.

MORNING, EFFIE.

GOOD MORNING, MS. FRIDAY. HE'S IN.

Michael Tree president

OR MAYBE YOU'VE HEARD ABOUT MIKE TREE— THE TOUGH, OLD-FASHIONED "PRIVATE EYE" WHO HIT IT BIG.

YOU'RE LATE.

2

WHAT ARE YOU GOING TO DO ABOUT IT, TOUGH GUY? FIRE A GIRL FOR BEING LATE, THE DAY SHE'S GETTING MARRIED?

"GIRL" IS SEXIST, MS. FRIDAY. YOU'RE THE ONE THAT TAUGHT ME THAT, REMEMBER?

SURE- AND I REMEMBER YOU TELLING ME "SEXIST" ISN'T REALLY A WORD--JUST SOMETHING SOME GODDAMN DYKE INVENTED.

BESIDES- I CAN BE ALLOWED A LITTLE "GIRLISHNESS" TODAY-

YOU MEAN YOU'LL TRADE IN "MS." FOR "MRS."?

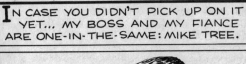

ARE YOU KIDDING? IT'LL BE MS. TREE, THANK YOU.

YOU'RE WELCOME.

IN CASE YOU DIDN'T PICK UP ON IT YET... MY BOSS AND MY FIANCE ARE ONE-IN-THE-SAME: MIKE TREE.

3

WE MET THREE YEARS AGO— WHEN I GAVE HIM A TICKET—

OKAY— I WON'T CONTEST THIS GODDAMN THING— ON ONE CONDITION...

SO YOUR NAME'S FRIDAY AND YOU'RE A COP?

THAT'S MS. FRIDAY TO YOU.

HE'D BEEN A COP, TOO, IT SEEMED, AND LEFT THE FORCE FOR PERSONAL REASONS, WHICH HE NEVER REVEALED...

WELL, YOU CAN CALL ME MR. TREE—

HE HAD A SMALL, ONE-MAN PRIVATE INVESTIGATION AGENCY, AND WAS STRUGGLING TO MAKE A GO OF IT.

THAT WAS NICE MS. FRIDAY.

NO ARGUMENT, MR. TREE.

WE HAD THINGS IN COMMON—

YOUR FIRST NAME IS MICHAEL?

FUNNY NAME FOR A WOMAN, HUH?

I DUNNO. MAYBE I'M JUST A GUY WITH THE FIRST NAME OF A GIRL...

BUT IT DIDN'T END WITH JUST OUR NAMES...

4

TAKE VIETNAM, FOR EXAMPLE— WE BOTH FOUGHT IT.

AND WE'D BOTH TRIED LAW SCHOOL— AND GAVE UP FOR LACK OF FUNDS...

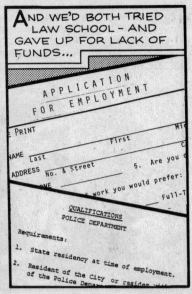

APPLICATION FOR EMPLOYMENT

Print

NAME   Last   First   Mi

ADDRESS   No. & Street   5. Are you

work you would prefer:

Full-T

QUALIFICATIONS
POLICE DEPARTMENT

Requirements:

1. State residency at time of employment.

2. Resident of the City or resides wit of the Police Depar

YOU'RE GETTING THE SHAFT— METER MAID! THAT'S THE LOWEST...

I'M NEXT IN LINE FOR PATROL CAR—

FORGET THAT SHIT. COME WORK WITH ME. I NEED YOU.

NEED ME? OR CAN "USE ME"? PLAYING SECRETARY IS NOT MY BAG—

HELL WITH THAT! YOU'D BE A FULL PARTNER— ALL IT TAKES TO LAND A P.I. TICKET IN THIS STATE IS A YEAR'S EXPERIENCE IN LAW ENFORCEMENT— AND YOU GOT THAT.

I GOT MY LICENSE, ALL RIGHT— AND MY GUN, TOO—

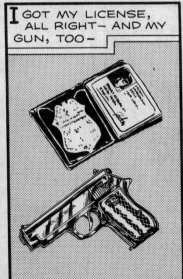

AND MY TYPEWRITER.

HOW'S IT COMIN', ANGEL?

5

OH, WELL – SOMEBODY HAD TO DO THE OFFICE WORK; KEEP THE RECORDS STRAIGHT; ORGANIZE MIKE TREE INTO A BUSINESS.

AND THEN HIS BREAK CAME – THE MASTERSON CASE – A SMALL-TOWN KID ACCUSED OF MURDERING HIS OWN MOTHER.

THEY'D GOTTEN A CONFESSION OUT OF THE KID, AND THE CONFUSED 18 YEAR-OLD WAS SENTENCED TO LIFE –

TILL A CIVIC GROUP, CONVINCED OF A MISCARRIAGE OF JUSTICE, WENT TO THE BIG CITY AND HIRED A PRIVATE EYE –

MIKE BUSTED THE CASE LIKE GLASS – AND FOUND THE EX-HUSBAND – THE BOY'S FATHER – WHO'D REALLY COMMITTED THE CRIME.

THEN CAME THE MEDIA – PEOPLE MAGAZINE – US – "60 MINUTES" – "20/20" – AND THE BESTSELLER –

I, THE EYE

by
Michael Tree

as told to Max Collins

The Story of a REAL Private Eye

THEN CAME MORE EMPLOYEES— LICENSED INVESTIGATORS DAN GREEN AND ROGER FREEMONT— EFFIE, OUR RECEPTIONIST AND— THANK GOD!— SECRETARY—

Michael Tree president

I REMAINED MIKE'S EXECUTIVE ASSISTANT, BUT NEVER TOOK FIELD ASSIGNMENTS; THE BUSINESS END OF A GUN HELD LESS INTEREST FOR ME THAN THE BUSINESS END OF THE BUSINESS—

AS FOR OUR PERSONAL RELATIONSHIP...

MIKE— WE'VE BEEN LOVERS FOR THREE YEARS, AND WE DON'T EVEN LIVE TOGETHER—

I'M JUST OLD-FASHIONED.

IF YOU'RE SO OLD-FASHIONED, WHY DIDN'T WE WAIT TILL WE WERE MARRIED?

I'VE BEEN AFRAID TO BRING MARRIAGE UP— AFRAID THAT ALL THAT FEMINIST BULLSHIT OF YOURS WOULD GET IN THE WAY—

WHY? 'CAUSE YOU'D WANT ME TO LEAVE THE BUSINESS? SETTLE DOWN AND HAVE YOUR KIDS?

WELL... YES.

I THOUGHT YOU'D NEVER ASK...

7

I MADE A COUPLE OF THINGS CLEAR TO MIKE: <u>ONE</u> CHILD, AND WHEN HE/SHE IS OF SCHOOL AGE, MS. TREE GOES BACK TO WORK...

RED? YOU WANT A <u>RED</u> WEDDING DRESS? TACKY, MICHAEL— REAL TACKY—

I SETTLED FOR OFF-WHITE.

WE FOUND A LITTLE CHAPEL OUTSIDE THE CITY AND ARRANGED A SMALL, PRIVATE SERVICE—

JUST MIKE, ME, THE PREACHER, EFFIE AS MAID OF HONOR, MIKE'S EX-PARTNER FROM HIS COP DAYS, CHICK STEELE.

WE'D ALLOWED JUST ONE NIGHT FOR OUR HONEYMOON IN A NEARBY MOTEL... SHORT BUT SWEET, MIKE SAID...

YOU'RE THIRSTY? I'LL GET YOU A CAN OF POP OUT OF THE MACHINE—

YOU'LL CATCH YOUR DEATH IN THAT RAIN—

IT'LL TAKE MORE THAN A LITTLE RAIN TO PUT OUT THIS GUY'S FIRE.

BANG BANG

TOMORROW?

8

TO BE CONTINUED—

Ms. TREE

"I, FOR AN EYE"
by Max Collins & Terry Beatty

Chapter Two

One Grave
for my Tears

© 1981 by Collins and Beatty

A FEW DAYS AGO, I HELD A SIMILAR BOUQUET - A BRIDAL ONE. I MISS YOU, MIKE.

1

HAS IT ONLY BEEN A WEEK SINCE YOU WERE MURDERED? HAS IT ONLY BEEN A WEEK SINCE THE DAY OUR LIFE TOGETHER WAS TO HAVE STARTED?

THE SUBURBAN COPS, AT THE SCENE, WERE COMPETENT ENOUGH...

WE CAN GET YOUR STATEMENT TOMORROW, MA'AM —

NO... JUST LET ME GET DRESSED...

YOUR FRIEND CHICK STEELE CAME FROM THE CITY — BEST MAN AT OUR WEDDING, HOURS — LIFETIMES — BEFORE. I CALLED HIM, AND HE CAME.

MICHAEL!

I HADN'T TOLD HIM ON THE PHONE — I JUST TOLD HIM IT WAS AN EMERGENCY...

MIKE'S DEAD — SOMEONE KILLED HIM, CHICK —

JESUS!

HE TOOK IT HARD. HE WAS YOUR PARTNER ON THE FORCE FOR THREE YEARS; THEY SAY THAT'S LIKE A MARRIAGE ITSELF.

I'LL FIND WHO DID IT, MICHAEL — I PROMISE YOU — AND MIKE —

NO, CHICK — NO.

2

IT'S MY *JOB* TO DO IT, MICHAEL — THESE SUBURBAN COPS ARE GOING TO NEED MY HELP —

NO DOUBT — BUT DO IT AS A *COP* — NOT OUT OF REVENGE.

CHICK DIDN'T UNDERSTAND — I DIDN'T WANT HIM TO.

YOU'RE QUITE A WOMAN, MICHAEL.

I ALREADY HAD THE *REVENGE* MARKET CORNERED.

THERE WAS NO FUNERAL — I KNEW YOU WOULDN'T WANT ONE — JUST A QUIET GRAVE-SIDE SERVICE — TWO SHORT DAYS AFTER YOUR DEATH...

STILL, THERE WAS SOMETHING OF A CROWD — YOU'D TOUCHED TOO MANY LIVES FOR IT TO BE OTHERWISE —

THE OFFICE STAFF APPROACHED ME, EN MASSE...

YOU TAKE ALL THE TIME YOU NEED —

NONSENSE. BUSINESS AS USUAL, TOMORROW, NINE O'CLOCK.

3

AND AT WORK THE NEXT DAY, THE PRESENCE OF YOU IN THE SURROUNDINGS WAS A COMFORT.

GOOD MORNING, EFFIE —

GOOD MORNING, MRS. TREE.

THAT'S MS. TREE, EFFIE — AND WE'LL BEGIN THE DAY BY MOVING MY THINGS INTO MIKE'S OFFICE.

YOU'RE GOING TO BE MY PERSONAL SECRETARY, FROM NOW ON, EFFIE — YOU'LL TAKE MY OLD OFFICE. PLACE AN AD FOR A NEW RECEPTIONIST.

WHAT'S GOING ON HERE?

WHAT DOES IT LOOK LIKE, ROGER?

WE'D LIKE TO TALK TO YOU ABOUT THAT, MS. TREE —

YOUR... HUSBAND APPROACHED US, A WEEK BEFORE YOU GOT HITCHED. HE SAID WITH YOU LEAVING THE BUSINESS TO HAVE BABIES, WE'D BE IN LINE FOR FULL PARTNERSHIP.

BUT IT LOOKS TO ME LIKE YOU'RE MOVING BACK IN, FULL TIME. I DON'T THINK I LIKE THAT.

REALLY?

4

I THINK YOU'RE OVERWROUGHT.

I THINK YOU'RE FIRED.

YOU *CAN'T* FIRE ME... I...

QUIT. YEAH. RIGHT. GOODBYE.

YOU COMIN', DAN? OR ARE YOU GONNA STICK AROUND AND SUCK UP TO THIS LOUSY BITCH?

I'LL STAY. I'D RATHER SUCK UP TO A LOUSY BITCH THAN HANG OUT WITH A TACTLESS ASSHOLE, ANYDAY.

SLAM

I THINK I HURT HIS FEELINGS.

THANK YOU FOR YOUR LOYALTY, DAN — I DON'T MIND WORKING FOR A WOMAN. BESIDES, YOU BEING BOSS IS PRACTICAL.

OH?

YEAH. WE WON'T EVEN HAVE TO CHANGE THE NAME ON THE DOOR.

Michael Tree president

5

PLACE ANOTHER AD, EFFIE - I'M IN THE MARKET FOR A FIRST-RATE INVESTIGATOR -

THERE'S A CALL FOR YOU - HE WON'T SAY HIS NAME.

THIS IS MS. TREE.

IT'S URGENT WE GET TOGETHER - I HAVE INFORMATION THAT MAY REGARD YOUR HUSBAND'S MURDER -

THAT "MAY" REGARD YOUR MURDER, THE MALE VOICE HAD SAID. IT WASN'T ENOUGH TO JUSTIFY A MEET - BUT I SET ONE UP ANYWAY...

I HAVEN'T BEEN TO THE ZOO SINCE I WAS A KID - I'M NOT CRAZY ABOUT THE SMELL...

MICHAEL TREE. I'D KNOW YOU ANYWHERE -

WELL I DON'T KNOW YOU...

MY NAME IS EDWARDS. YOUR HUSBAND WAS WORKING FOR ME AT THE TIME OF HIS DEATH.

I DON'T BELIEVE YOU. I WAS MY HUSBAND'S BUSINESS PARTNER - I WAS AWARE OF EVERY CASE HE TOOK ON...

NOT EVERY CASE -

6

I'M AN ASSISTANT DISTRICT ATTORNEY. I EMPLOYED YOUR HUSBAND OUT OF MY OWN POCKET, TO UNDERTAKE A CONFIDENTIAL INVESTIGATION OF...
BANG
MR. EDWARDS!
BANG
BANG
7

CHICK ARRIVED AND CONFIRMED __SOME__ OF EDWARDS' STORY —

HE WAS AN ASSISTANT D.A., ALL RIGHT. WHY HE'D HIRE A PRIVATE DETECTIVE IS ANYBODY'S GUESS.

I'D NEVER KILLED ANYBODY BEFORE —

WHO WAS HE?

I DON'T KNOW HIM. MY GUESS IS HE'S OUT-OF-TOWN TALENT. POSSIBLY MIKE'S MURDERER.

KNOWING THAT DIDN'T FEEL AS GOOD AS IT SHOULD —

IF HE'S JUST SOME HIRED KILLER, THEN IT ISN'T ENOUGH...

IF SOMEONE HIRED YOUR MURDER, MIKE, THEN MY WORK IS JUST BEGINNING ...

OH... EXCUSE ME —

MICHAEL TRE BELOVED HUSBAN 1947 — 198

8

TO BE CONTINUED ———

Ms. TREE

"I, FOR AN EYE"
by Max Collins & Terry Beatty

Chapter Three

© 1981 by Collins and Beatty

DEATH IS A LITTLE BLACK BOOK

HOW MUCH HAVE YOU KEPT FROM ME, MIKE? WHAT SECRETS DID YOU HAVE?

AT THE CEMETERY, AS I'M LAYING FLOWERS AT YOUR GRAVE, ANOTHER WOMAN APPROACHES AND DOES THE SAME... AND IS GONE BEFORE I CAN STOP HER... AND ASK HER...

1

ASK HER WHY SHE MOURNS MY HUSBAND'S DEATH? MY HUSBAND OF A DAY, SHOT DOWN IN THE NIGHT...

MICHAEL TREE
BELOVED HUSBAND
1947 — 1981

AND WHAT OF EDWARDS, MIKE? THE ASSISTANT D.A. YOU WERE WORKING ON A CASE FOR — A CASE YOU HADN'T SHARED WITH ME — YOUR PARTNER; YOUR BRIDE...

EVEN YOUR EX-PARTNER FROM YOUR DAYS ON THE FORCE DIDN'T KNOW ABOUT EDWARDS. YOUR FRIEND, CHICK STEELE —

I'VE CHECKED WITH THE D.A., MICHAEL — ANY INVESTIGATION INITIATED BY EDWARDS WAS STRICTLY UNOFFICIAL...

SOMETHING IN EDWARDS' PERSONAL LIFE, PERHAPS. MAYBE YOU'LL WANT TO FOLLOW THAT UP ON YOUR OWN.

WHAT ABOUT THE MAN I KILLED? THE ONE WHO KILLED EDWARDS?

AS I SUSPECTED, AN OUT-OF-TOWN HITTER... BOB RANDISI. FREELANCER WITH SYNDICATE TIES.

HOW ABOUT YOUR OWN INVESTIGATION OF MIKE'S MURDER?

NOTHING, YET. THERE'S A LONG LIST OF ENEMIES FROM HIS P.D. DAYS.

I'LL STAY IN TOUCH, CHICK — THANKS.

DO THAT — YOU GOT A COUPLE INQUESTS TO ATTEND, YOU KNOW —

2

I TALKED WITH MRS. EDWARDS —

NO, I CAN'T THINK OF ANY REASON CARL MIGHT'VE HIRED A PRIVATE DETECTIVE...

HE WAS A LITTLE UNHAPPY AT WORK, I KNOW — BUT AS FAR AS HIS HOME LIFE WAS CONCERNED, HE — WE — WERE VERY HAPPY. NO... NO PROBLEMS AT ALL —

I KNEW HOW SHE FELT. SHE'D LOST A HUSBAND.

YOU... KILLED THE MAN WHO SHOT CARL, DIDN'T YOU?

YES — BUT THE PERSON OR PERSONS WHO HIRED THAT MAN ARE STILL AT LARGE.

BUT I'LL FIND WHOEVER IT WAS — I PROMISE YOU THAT.

WHAT GOOD WILL IT DO? WILL IT BRING CARL BACK? OR YOUR HUSBAND? DOES IT FIX ANYTHING?

IT'S A START.

3

I TRIED TO GET IN TO SEE THE D.A., BUT HE WAS TOO BUSY—

WHO **CAN** I SEE?

MR. EDWARDS WORKED CLOSELY WITH MS. WORTH.

DISTRICT ATTORNEY

MS. WORTH, LIKE EDWARDS, WAS AN ASSISTANT D.A. – MARY WORTH WAS HER NAME, LIKE IN THE COMICS; BUT THIS MARY WORTH DIDN'T WANT TO HELP...

I DON'T KNOW WHAT YOU'RE TALKING ABOUT.

ANY INVESTIGATION MR. EDWARDS WAS INVOLVED IN **OFFICIALLY**, I WOULD KNOW ABOUT. IF HE HIRED YOUR HUSBAND TO WORK FOR HIM, IT'S THE FIRST I'VE HEARD OF IT.

IF I'D BEEN IN THE JURY BOX LISTENING TO THAT SUMMATION, I WOULDN'T HAVE BOUGHT IT: SHE WAS LYING – RIGHT DOWN TO THE TREMOR IN HER VOICE.

ALLOW ME TO SHOW YOU OUT –

CONSIDER THIS, MS. TREE – IF CARL EDWARDS **WAS** UNDERTAKING A **SUB ROSA** INQUIRY – AND I **DID** KNOW – WOULD IT BE WISE TO ADMIT IT, AFTER WHAT HAPPENED TO CARL?

YOU'D HAVE COMPLETE CONFIDENTIALITY ON MY PART – MY PROTECTION...

OH – DO YOU MEAN YOU'LL TRACK DOWN **MY** KILLER, TOO? GOOD DAY, MS. TREE.

4

IT WAS LATE AFTERNOON WHEN I FINALLY GOT TO MY OWN OFFICE ...

ANYTHING IMPORTANT TODAY, EFFIE?

WE'RE GETTING APPLICATIONS IN FOR THE RECEPTIONIST'S JOB —

YOU SOUND ANXIOUS TO START YOUR NEW JOB AS MY ASSISTANT.

GUILTY. DAN GREEN'S BEEN ASKING ONCE EVERY 15 MINUTES IF YOU'RE IN YET. WANTS TO TALK —

SEND HIM IN IMMEDIATELY.

IS THIS FAST ENOUGH?

SINCE YOU CANNED ROGER FREEMONT, I'M ASS-DEEP IN WORK — WE NEED ANOTHER INVESTIGATOR, FAST.

AND I'M NOT CARRYING MY OWN WEIGHT, EITHER — IS THAT IT?

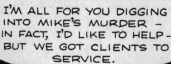

I'M ALL FOR YOU DIGGING INTO MIKE'S MURDER — IN FACT, I'D LIKE TO HELP — BUT WE GOT CLIENTS TO SERVICE.

FAIR ENOUGH. LET'S SUB-CONTRACT SOME WORK TO MIST INVESTIGATIONS, TILL WE FIND A REPLACEMENT FOR FREEMONT. NOW — I HAVE SOME QUESTIONS...

5

I FILLED DAN IN ON WHAT HAD BEEN HAPPENING —

I DON'T KNOW ANYTHING ABOUT ANY INVESTIGATIONS MIKE MIGHT HAVE BEEN WORKING ON, BESIDES THE REGULAR STUFF —

AND AS FOR THE BLONDE AT MIKE'S GRAVESIDE - FORGIVE ME - HE WAS A HEALTHY GUY. YOU WEREN'T THE FIRST WOMAN HE EVER MET.

DAN WAS RIGHT. YOU WERE TOO GOOD A LOVER NOT TO HAVE BEEN AROUND - I FORGAVE YOU THE BLONDE - FOR THE MOMENT.

I ALMOST FORGOT - YOU HAD A CALL FROM THE SUBURBAN P.D. THAT HANDLED MIKE'S...

DEATH. THEY HAVE SOME THINGS OF HIS - PERSONAL EFFECTS.

THAT REMINDED ME - I NEEDED TO GO TO YOUR APARTMENT - CLEAN IT OUT. I HADN'T FACED THAT YET. WE WERE GOING TO LIVE THERE...

I CLIMBED THE STAIRS TO YOUR FOURTH-FLOOR LOFT APARTMENT - AND WHEN I UNLOCKED THE DOOR AND STEPPED IN —

6

SOMEBODY HAD BEEN LOOKING FOR SOMETHING, MIKE —

OR STILL WAS —

BUMP!

THE NOISE CAME FROM THE BEDROOM —

POW!

BANG

HE WAS GONE — HE LOOKED LIKE A "HE," ANYWAY, FROM THE GLIMPSE OF THE STOCKY FORM I GOT —

7

THE QUESTION IS, DID HE FIND WHAT HE WAS LOOKING FOR?

THAT'S JUST ONE QUESTION, CHICK — ANOTHER IS WHAT WAS HE LOOKING FOR? WHAT THE HELL WAS HE LOOKING FOR?

ARE YOU OKAY, MICHAEL?

YEAH. ARE YOUR PRINT BOYS ABOUT DONE? I WANT TO STRAIGHTEN THE PLACE UP.

WHAT HAD THE STOCKY FIGURE BEEN LOOKING FOR? THAT THOUGHT PULSED IN MY BRAIN, THROUGH THE NIGHT — THROUGH THE NEXT DAY, AS I DROVE OUT TO THE SUBURBS —

HERE'S HIS STUFF, MRS. TREE — KEYS, MONEY, COMB, WATCH — AND SOME KIND OF BOOK. SIGN FOR IT, WOULD YA?

ADDRESSES and NUMBERS

8

TO BE CONTINUED

Chapter Four

If a Tree Falls...

© 1981 by Collins and Beatty

NAMES... ADDRESSES... PEOPLE I'VE NEVER KNOWN— BUT YOU DID, MIKE...

THIS BOOK - THIS LIST OF PEOPLE AND PLACES - IT'S THE **ANSWER**, MIKE, ISN'T IT?

THE ANSWER TO WHY THEY KILLED YOU THAT NIGHT, THAT RAINY NIGHT THAT SHOULD'VE BEEN OUR HONEYMOON...

CARL EDWARDS... THE ASSISTANT D.A. YOU WERE WORKING FOR, WITHOUT MY KNOWLEDGE -

ADDRESSES

NAME Carl Edwards
STREET 125 Palermo
CITY
ZIP CODE
PHONE 606-08

THE MAN THE HITMAN KILLED AT THE ZOO - THE HITMAN I THEN KILLED -

EFFIE, IS DAN GREEN IN? PUT HIM ON... DAN, I WANT YOU TO MEET ME AT MIKE'S APARTMENT -

YOU TRUSTED DAN GREEN; OR SO YOU TOLD ME. HAD YOU TRUSTED HIM MORE THAN ME?

I THOUGHT THIS PLACE GOT TORN UP -

IT DID - I STRAIGHTENED UP, AFTER... THEY WERE LOOKING FOR SOMETHING, DAN.

DOESN'T TAKE A HELL OF A DETECTIVE TO FIGURE THAT, MS. TREE - TELL ME SOMETHING...

2

WHY ARE WE MEETING HERE, INSTEAD OF THE OFFICE?

WE MIGHT BE GETTING INTO AN EXTRA-LEGAL AREA, DAN — AND AS LICENSED REPRESENTATIVES OF THE COURT, WE CAN'T RISK PLAYING THAT GAME AT THE OFFICE.

I FIGURED AS MUCH. I CAN FIGURE SOMETHING ELSE, TOO: YOU'VE FOUND WHAT THEY DIDN'T —

SUPPOSE I HAD. SUPPOSE I'D FOUND A BOOK OF NAMES AND ADDRESSES — NAMES OF PEOPLE I HAD NO KNOWLEDGE OF, IN TERMS OF MIKE'S BUSINESS OR HIS PERSONAL LIFE.

CONSIDERING AN ASSISTANT D.A.'S DEAD, I'D SAY THAT BOOK SHOULD BE TURNED OVER TO THE COPS —

IF I TOLD LT. STEELE ABOUT IT, HE'D WANT THE BOOK — AND TO HANDLE THE INVESTIGATION HIMSELF.

AND YOU WANT TO HANG ONTO THIS HYPOTHETICAL BOOK — AND HYPOTHETICAL INVESTIGATION — YOURSELF, RIGHT?

RIGHT.

THEN DO IT WITHOUT ME. I WISH YOU LUCK, MS. TREE — BUT I HAVE TO GET BACK TO THE OFFICE — SOMEBODY SHOULD...

3

DAN WAS RIGHT – HE WAS COVERING FOR ME AT THE AGENCY, AND EVEN AS HIS BOSS, I COULDN'T EXPECT MORE...

AND IT SEEMED APPARENT HE'D HAD NO PRIOR KNOWLEDGE OF THE ADDRESS BOOK – YOU HAD KEPT THAT FROM DAN JUST AS YOU DID FROM ME –

ISN'T THAT GREAT NEWS? YOU DIDN'T TRUST ME WITH THIS, BUT YOU DIDN'T TRUST DAN EITHER – SO I SHOULDN'T FEEL BAD...

SMACK

GODDAMN YOU, MIKE. DAMN YOU FOR KEEPING THIS FROM ME –

DAMN YOU – DAMN YOU FOR...

DYING.

4

I STARTED WITH PAGE ONE OF THE BOOK— WHICH WAS ALPHABETIZED: YOU WERE NOTHING IF NOT METHODICAL, MIKE—

THE FIRST NAME WASN'T A PERSON, IT WAS A BUSINESS — APPLE DETECTIVE AGENCY — A RUNDOWN OFFICE BUILDING IN A BLOCK THAT RAN TO FLOPHOUSES—

NOT A PRESTIGIOUS AGENCY, IT WOULD SEEM — CONSIDERING I WAS IN THE SAME BUSINESS AND HAD NEVER HEARD OF IT BEFORE; BUT PERHAPS YOU SUBCONTRACTED SOME WORK HERE, MIKE—

COME.

KNOCK KNOCK

IT WAS JUST A SMALL SINGLE ROOM — NO OUTER OFFICE — NO RECEPTIONIST — NO SECRETARY—

JUST THE DETECTIVE WHO RAN THE PLACE—

ROGER!

HOW THE HELL—

ROGER FREEMONT. THE OPERATIVE WHO'D BEEN WITH OUR AGENCY THREE YEARS, ONLY TO BE FIRED BY ME THE DAY AFTER YOUR FUNERAL, MIKE — WHEN HE GOT INSOLENT.

HE HADN'T CHANGED.

GET YOUR BUTT OUT OF HERE—

5

NICE TO SEE YOU AGAIN, TOO, ROGER — I SEE YOU'RE DOING WELL.

SARCASTIC BROADS GIVE ME A PAIN IN THE ASS. TAKE A HIKE —

MAYBE I HAVE SOME WORK FOR YOU. MAYBE I WANT YOU TO COME BACK TO WORK FOR ME.

LOOK, MRS. TREE OR MS. TREE OR WHATEVER THE HELL — I GOT A NICE LITTLE BUSINESS STARTED HERE, SINCE LEAVING YOUR EMPLOY — STARTING AT THE BOTTOM, MAYBE, BUT...

HOW IS IT THIS BUSINESS YOU STARTED AFTER I FIRED YOU IS LISTED IN THIS —

THIS BOOK OF ADDRESSES MIKE HAD ON HIM THE NIGHT HE WAS MURDERED —

I THOUGHT MAYBE MIKE MIGHT'VE KEPT SOMETHING LIKE THIS. LOOK — WE BETTER TALK. SIT DOWN...

6

ROGER —

A SILENCED BULLET — FROM THE ROOFTOP ACROSS THE WAY, LIKELY — A RIFLE, NO DOUBT —

THE BULLET HAD GONE THROUGH ROGER — I WAS LUCKY I DIDN'T GET SLOPPY SECONDS —

ROGER WAS LUCKY, TOO — HE WAS STILL ALIVE —

AMBULANCE — GUNSHOT WOUND IN CHEST — BRADBURY BUILDING, SUITE 714 — HURRY!

CHICK STEELE CAUGHT UP WITH ME AT THE HOSPITAL —

WE FOUND AN EJECTED SHELL ON THE OPPOSITE ROOFTOP — AS YOU SUSPECTED. BUT NO WITNESSES.

AND I COULDN'T PURSUE WHOEVER IT WAS — HAD TO STAY WITH ROGER.

HOW IS ROGER?

COMA. I WAS JUST LEAVING.

7

SOME OF THE NAMES IN THE BOOK DIDN'T SEEM TO BE BUSINESS-RELATED — ONE, AT LEAST, SEEMED TO BE PERSONAL — A RELATIVE...

ANNE TREE. A SISTER? AN AUNT, A COUSIN, PERHAPS. SHE LIVED IN A QUIETLY MIDDLE-CLASS NEIGHBORHOOD IN THE SUBURBS —

AFTER WHAT WENT DOWN AT ROGER'S OFFICE, I HAD GONE ON TO THE APPARENT RELATIVE, TO GET HER OUT OF THE WAY, TO RULE HER OUT —

KNOCK

BUT NO ONE WAS HOME. LIKE ANY GOOD DETECTIVE, I FOUND A WINDOW TO PEEK IN...

THE WOMAN AT THE CEMETERY — THE WOMAN WHO LEFT THE FLOWERS ON YOUR GRAVE, MIKE —

LADY — WHAT ARE YOU DOIN'? WHO ARE YOU?

MY NAME'S MICHAEL TREE. WHAT'S YOUR NAME?

ARE YOU KIDDIN' OR SOMETHING, LADY?

THAT'S *MY* NAME — MIKE TREE, JR.

8

TO BE CONTINUED —

Ms. TREE

"I, FOR AN EYE"
by Max Collins & Terry Beatty

MIKE, GO NEXT DOOR AND ASK TOMMY'S MOTHER IF YOU AND HE CAN PLAY — IN HIS YARD —

MOM, HOW COME SHE HAS MY NAME?

NEVER MIND, NOW SCOOT — WE'LL TALK LATER —

AW... OKAY. 'BYE LADY.

I'VE BEEN WONDERING WHEN... IF... YOU'D FIND ME. LET'S GO INSIDE AND TALK.

I WANTED TO SAY SOMETHING AT THE CEMETERY THAT DAY — BUT I LOST MY NERVE — RUSHED AWAY —

MIKE DIDN'T SAY MUCH ABOUT YOU — BUT I DO KNOW HE LOVED YOU VERY MUCH... YOU HAVE TO BELIEVE THAT. CAN I GET YOU SOMETHING? COFFEE? TEA...?

JUST WHO THE HELL ARE YOU?

DON'T YOU KNOW? I'M YOUR HUSBAND'S FIRST WIFE.

2

AND SOMETH[...]
HIM... SEVE[...]
OVER THERE [...]
"CALIFORNIA GIRLS [...]
MARRIED THEM BEFORE THEY
SHIPPED OVER, FOR THE MONTHLY
PAYCHECKS - FOR THE BENEFITS -
DEATH BENEFITS, OFTEN -

HIS FA[...]

"AND THAT'S WHAT HE DID THINK. HE THOUGHT I MARRIED HIM BECAUSE I WAS ALREADY 'TWO MONTHS GONE,' HE SAID. HE DIDN'T THINK MIKE JR. WAS HIS."

I DIDN'T ASK FOR CHILD SUPPORT OR ALIMONY - MY PARENTS WERE STILL ALIVE THEN - I STAYED WITH THEM - MARRIED AGAIN - NONE OF THAT MATTERS...

ABOUT A YEAR AGO, I MOVED HERE - I'D BEEN OUT OF TOUCH WITH MIKE SINCE OUR DIVORCE. I CONTACTED HIM, FOR HELP. HE GAVE IT...

"AND HE SAW MIKE JR., AND I THINK FOR THE FIRST TIME REALIZED THE BOY WAS HIS..."

4

THERE WAS NO RENEWED ROMANCE BETWEEN US. HE FELT NOTHING FOR ME - HE <u>LOVED</u> YOU. AND WOULD'VE TOLD YOU ABOUT ME AND MIKE IN TIME.

YOU STILL LOVE HIM, DON'T YOU?

TOMMY'S MOM SAYS I GOTTA COME HOME NOW, SO I'M HOME. ARE YOU AND THE LADY THROUGH TALKING?

YES. WE ARE, MIKE.

ARE YOU IN THE MOVIES, LADY? YOU LOOK LIKE A MOVIE STAR OR SOMETHING -

DID YOU KNOW MY FATHER? IS THAT WHY WE GOT THE SAME NAME? ARE WE RELATED?

MIKE! PLEASE!

WE AREN'T RELATED, MIKE. I WISH WE WERE.

5

WHY DID YOU KEEP IT FROM ME, MIKE? THIS, AND SO MANY OTHER SECRETS? A SON, MIKE —

MICHAEL TREE
(HER HUSBAND)
?? — 1981

I THOUGHT I MIGHT FIND YOU HERE

CHICK! WHAT —?

CAN WE TALK? ABOUT THE CASE? I HAVE SOME INFORMATION YOU MIGHT BE INTERESTED IN —

ALL RIGHT. I'LL MEET YOU AT YOUR OFFICE IN FIFTEEN MINUTES.

NO. THAT WOULDN'T DO...

I DON'T WANT TO ANTAGONIZE THE SITUATION — MY SUPERIORS ARE ALREADY WONDERING WHY EVERY TIME THERE'S A SHOOTING IN THIS TOWN, YOU ARE AT THE SCENE —

CHICK SENT HIS DRIVER ON, AND I DROVE US TO HIS APARTMENT — I WASN'T UP TO A RESTAURANT OR ANY OTHER PUBLIC PLACE —

HOW'S ROGER FREEMONT DOING?

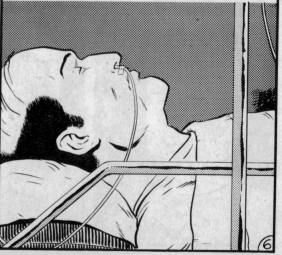

"STILL IN A COMA. I'VE GOT A MAN ON HIS DOOR AT THE HOSPITAL, 24 HOURS."

6

THAT'S ONE OF THE THINGS I HAD TO TELL YOU: THAT OFFICE ROGER WAS WORKING OUT OF WAS LEASED MONTHS AGO - BY ONE MICHAEL TREE -

CHICK DIDN'T KNOW JUST HOW MANY MICHAEL TREES THERE WERE IN THIS CASE -

OF COURSE, THAT'S THE MALE MICHAEL TREE I REFER TO -

DO YOU KNOW ANY REASON WHY MIKE WOULD'VE RENTED THAT OFFICE? WITHOUT YOUR KNOWLEDGE?

THERE ARE A LOT OF THINGS MIKE DID THAT I DIDN'T KNOW ABOUT.

YOU KNOW THEN? ABOUT MIKE'S FIRST MARRIAGE?

CHICK KNEW. I DIDN'T. YOUR EX-PARTNER FROM THE FORCE, YOU TRUSTED. NOT ME.

AND WHEN ANNE TURNED UP AGAIN, AND HE SAW THAT KID - AND KNEW IT WAS HIS...

WELL, HE FIGURED HE'D MARRY YOU, AND THEN SPRING THIS ON YOU. YOU KNOW MIKE - HE FIGURED YOU'D BE PISSED, BUT NOT DIVORCE HIM OR ANYTHING.

7

YOU MISS HIM, TOO, DON'T YOU?

YEAH.

I DON'T KNOW WHY IT HAPPENED, MIKE — WHETHER LONELINESS DID IT — OR MAYBE I THOUGHT GETTING CLOSE TO YOUR BEST FRIEND WOULD BE LIKE GETTING CLOSE TO YOU —

OR MAYBE I JUST WANTED TO GET EVEN.

8

TO BE CONTINUED ————

Ms. TREE

"I, FOR AN EYE"
by Max Collins & Terry Beatty

Chapter Six — KISS TOMORROW HELLO

©1982 by Collins and Beatty

1

I DON'T KNOW HOW LONG I WAS OUT— WHEN I WOKE UP, CHICK WAS AT MY SIDE...

ARE YOU OKAY, MICHAEL?

DID YOU STOP HIM? DID YOU GET HIM?

NO – I GRABBED MY GUN AND WENT AFTER HIM, BUT WHEN I GOT OUT TO THE HALL, HE WAS GONE...

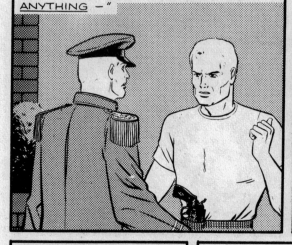

"I LOOKED DOWN THE STAIRWELL AND SAW NO SIGN OF HIM – SO I TOOK THE ELEVATOR DOWN AND QUESTIONED THE DOORMAN, AND HE HADN'T SEEN ANYTHING –"

"BUT THERE'S A SERVICE ENTRANCE IN BACK, AND AN ALLEY BEHIND THE BUILDING," CHICK CONTINUED, "AND I CAUGHT A GLIMPSE OF A CAR PULLING OUT OF THE ALLEY, FAST – COULD'VE BEEN HIM."

NO PARKING

DID YOU GET THE LICENSE NUMBER? THE MAKE?

I DIDN'T CATCH THE LICENSE, BUT IT WAS A DATSUN 280 ZX, CANDY-APPLE RED. WHOEVER IT WAS, HE MAKES GOOD DOUGH FOR A CAT BURGLAR.

IS THAT WHAT HE WAS?

WHAT ELSE?

HE WENT STRAIGHT FOR MY PURSE, CHICK – HE KNEW WHAT HE WAS AFTER –

2

WELL, MIKE, I ENDED UP IN YOUR BEST FRIEND'S BED; AND REVENGE WAS SWEET — BUT GETTING EVEN WITH YOU FOR WHAT YOU HELD BACK FROM ME — NAMELY, A PREVIOUS WIFE AND A SON — WAS SMALL STAKES.

FINDING YOUR KILLER WAS STILL TOP PRIORITY — AND I COULD'VE KICKED MYSELF: I HAD THE KILLER IN MY GRASP, AT CHICK'S, AND LOST HIM...

BUT MY STOCKY FRIEND, WHOEVER HE WAS — AND HE WAS ALMOST CERTAINLY THE SAME INTRUDER WHO'D TAKEN A SHOT AT ME AFTER RANSACKING YOUR APARTMENT, NOT LONG AGO — NOW HAD THE BOOK...

ONLY I DID, TOO.

HELLO, MS. TREE.

EFFIE, GET ME THE ENVELOPE MARKED "PERSONAL FILE" FROM THE SAFE, WOULD YOU?

Tree Investigations Inc.

I HAD PHOTOCOPIED THE BOOK, JUST TO PLAY IT SAFE — SO WHILE I HAD SHARED MY KNOWLEDGE, MIKE, I HADN'T LOST IT...

THE QUESTION WAS, DID SOMEONE LISTED IN THIS BOOK WANT IT? OR DID SOMEONE WANT THE NAMES TO START KILLING — THE FIRST NAME I'D CALLED ON, ROGER FREEMONT, LAY NEAR DEATH —

4

CAN I HAVE A MINUTE, MS. TREE, I – JESUS, WHAT HAPPENED TO YOU?

JUST A LOVE PAT, DAN. SIT DOWN.

CAN YOU EXPLAIN TO ME WHY ROGER WAS SHOT?

THIS CASE, WHATEVER IT WAS, WAS SO CONFIDENTIAL, SO DANGEROUS, THE REST OF US IN THE AGENCY COULDN'T BE LET IN ON IT –

SO MIKE AND ROGER OPENED A SEPARATE OFFICE, IN THAT FLOPHOUSE DISTRICT, TO FURTHER ISOLATE THE INVESTIGATION?

THAT'S RIGHT. AND WHEN THE CASE DID PROVE AS DANGEROUS AS THEIR PRECAUTIONS WOULD INDICATE THEY BELIEVED...

ROGER PULLED THAT STUNT, AFTER THE FUNERAL – BEING SUCH AN OBNOXIOUS ASSHOLE YOU'D HAVE TO FIRE HIM.

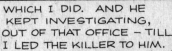

WHICH I DID. AND HE KEPT INVESTIGATING, OUT OF THAT OFFICE – TILL I LED THE KILLER TO HIM.

WHAT CAN I DO, MS. TREE? IT'S TIME I GOT INTO THIS...

5

I'VE GOT A JOB I THINK YOU'LL LIKE — HOW 'BOUT DRIVING A BEAUTIFUL BLONDE SOMEPLACE, AND HIDING OUT WITH HER?

WHAT'S THE CATCH?

HER ELEVEN YEAR-OLD SON'LL BE ALONG.

TERRIFIC.

I SENT DAN OFF TO GET HIS SUITCASE — AND GUN — AND CAUGHT ANNE TREE AT HOME —

ANNE, THIS IS MICHAEL TREE — I WANT YOU TO LISTEN CAREFULLY —

DROP EVERYTHING? GET MIKE OUT OF SCHOOL?

I THINK YOUR LIFE MAY BE IN DANGER — I'M SENDING AN OPERATIVE TO PUT YOU IN MY PROTECTIVE CUSTODY —

DON'T SAY I NEVER DID YOU ANY FAVORS, SMARTASS —

EVERYONE ON THAT LIST STOOD TO BE IN DANGER — I STARTED IN ON THE NAMES I HADN'T CONTACTED YET —

IT WAS MID-DAY AS I TRIED HER BUSINESS NUMBER —

IS MS. SMITHERS IN? NO? SHE'S AT HOME? HER MARRIED NAME IS WHAT?

6

I'M IN FAVOR OF YOU GOING INTO HIDING, FOR A DAY OR TWO AT LEAST —

THEN GET OUT OF OUR WAY.

DON'T BULLY ME, LADY — I'M NOT YOUR HUSBAND!

I WANT SOME ANSWERS.

WELL... WHAT ARE THE QUESTIONS?

WHAT SUB ROSA INVESTIGATION WAS ASSISTANT D.A. EDWARDS UNDERTAKING WITH MY HUSBAND'S HELP — AND YOURS?

WHAT DO YOU THINK? CITY CORRUPTION — GRAFT. IT INCLUDED OUR OWN BOSS, THE D.A.

SPECIFICALLY.

SPECIFICALLY, WE KNEW OF A CASE INVOLVING MOB HIGHER-UPS THAT SHOULD'VE GONE TO TRIAL. IT DIDN'T. THE EVIDENCE... WELL, IT DISAPPEARED.

8

TAKE A LOOK AT THIS — TELL ME HOW MANY NAMES YOU RECOGNIZE. IN THE MEANTIME, DO YOU MIND IF I USE YOUR PHONE?

CAN I STOP YOU?

EFFIE, HAVE YOU HEARD FROM DAN? GOOD. GOOD.

THERE'S A MESSAGE HERE FROM THE HOSPITAL. ROGER FREEMONT HAS COME OUT OF HIS COMA, AND WANTS TO TALK TO YOU...

I THINK THAT CAN BE ARRANGED. THANKS, EFFIE.

WELL? I KNOW ALL THE NAMES EXCEPT ONE: ANNE TREE. IS SHE A RELATIVE?

YES. AND THE OTHERS? WITNESSES, INFORMANTS, SOME OF THEM WITHIN CITY GOVERNMENT. IT'S THE CASE EDWARDS AND YOUR HUSBAND BUILT.

HAVE YOU DEALT WITH THESE PEOPLE? ARE YOU WILLING TO TAKE THE TIME TO WARN THEM?

9

MARY WORTH AGREED TO HELP. I TOLD HER TO DRIVE TO THE MOTEL WHERE SHE AND HER HUSBAND WERE PLANNING TO HIDE OUT, AND THEN MAKE HER PHONE CALLS... I LEFT THE PHOTOCOPIES WITH HER — I HAD ANOTHER SET —

DOCTOR — I'M HERE TO SEE ROGER FREEMONT.

YES — MS. TREE? YES, HE ASKED TO SEE YOU. GO ON —

EXCUSE ME, I'M MS. TREE — I'M HERE TO SEE FREEMONT.

OH, YES — I'M DETECTIVE HARTOG.

I'M SORRY, BUT FREEMONT JUST HAD A RELAPSE — ONE OF THE DOCTORS IS IN THERE WITH HIM NOW.

BUT —

WAIT DOWNSTAIRS AND I'LL HAVE YOU PAGED WHEN YOU CAN SEE HIM...

10

WHAT — WHAT DO YOU WANT?

SOME ANSWERS.

HE GAVE THEM TO ME. SO DID ROGER.

WHO — WHO DID YOU TURN HARTOG OVER TO?

I CALLED CHAMBERS, WITH INTERNAL AFFAIRS.

GOOD. HE'S NASTY, BUT TRUSTWORTHY.

NOW THAT YOU KNOW, WHAT ARE YOU... WHAT DO YOU PLAN TO... DO?

HANDLE IT MYSELF, OF COURSE.

THEN WHAT?

THEN I'M GOING TO TELL EFFIE TO CANCEL OUR AD FOR A NEW INVESTIGATOR.

BECAUSE YOU'RE COMING BACK TO WORK FOR ME, WHEN YOU'RE THROUGH LOAFING...

12

MICHAEL – WHAT ARE YOU DOING HERE? CAN I COME IN?

OF COURSE. WHAT'S UP? YOUR HANDS, FUCKER.

MICHAEL? SHUT-UP. SHUT-UP. LET ME DECIDE IF I WANT TO SEE YOU DIE SLOW OR JUST DIE.

I DON'T KNOW IF I CAN EVER GET RID OF THE SICK FEELING I HAVE, FROM HAVING MADE IT WITH YOU. I COULD USE A BATH RIGHT NOW – MAYBE A BLOOD BATH WOULD DO...

MICHAEL – YOU'RE WRONG. WHAT YOU'RE THINKING, IT'S WRONG.

NO. YOUR STOCKY STOOGE HARTOG TOLD ME. SO DID ROGER. AND SO DOES THE REST OF THE EVIDENCE, CIRCUMSTANTIAL THOUGH IT MAY BE.

"MIKE NEVER TOLD ME WHY HE QUIT THE FORCE – 'PERSONAL REASONS,' HE SAID – MY GUESS IS HE FOUND OUT YOU WERE KNEE-DEEP IN GRAFT AND COULDN'T TURN YOU IN..."

"BUT YOU STAYED FRIENDS, NEVERTHELESS – YOU WERE EVEN BEST MAN AT HIS WEDDING, HOURS BEFORE YOU LED A HITMAN TO HIM!"

MICHAEL, IT'S THE MOB – I ADMIT I'M DIRTY. BUT I DIDN'T SET MIKE UP. THE MOB DID IT ALL!

13

I DON'T THINK SO. I THINK YOU ASKED THE MOB FOR HELP, NOT THE OTHER WAY AROUND.

YOU WERE THE FOCUS OF THE INVESTIGATION, NOT THE MOB — YOU AND OTHER CROOKED COPS AND THE CROOKED D.A.

I LOVED MIKE. I WOULDN'T HURT HIM.

SHUT-UP! YOU HAD HIM KILLED, CHICK!

I SHOULD HAVE KNOWN — I SHOULD HAVE KNOWN AN INVESTIGATION LAUNCHED SECRETLY BY AN ASSISTANT D.A. WOULD INVOLVE CITY CORRUPTION —

"BUT YOU TRIED TO SEND ME DOWN A BLIND ALLEY, LOOKING INTO EDWARD'S PRIVATE LIFE, CHICK — WHEN ALL HIS WIFE COULD SAY WAS HE WAS 'UNHAPPY AT WORK'! WITH A CROOKED BOSS, WHY SHOULDN'T HE BE?"

WHAT SHOULD REALLY HAVE TOLD ME WAS MIKE'S FAILING TO TELL YOU, HIS BEST FRIEND, ABOUT THE SUB ROSA INVESTIGATION —

HE TOLD YOU EVERYTHING ELSE. YOU KNEW ABOUT ANNE TREE AND LITTLE MIKE. BUT HE COULDN'T TRUST YOU WITH THIS PROBLEM — BECAUSE HE'D DISCOVERED YOU WERE THE PROBLEM.

14

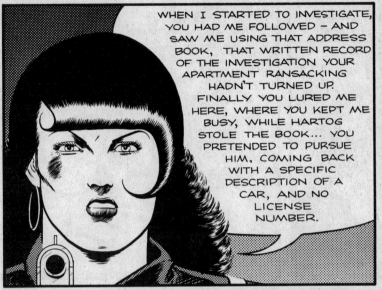

WHEN I STARTED TO INVESTIGATE, YOU HAD ME FOLLOWED — AND SAW ME USING THAT ADDRESS BOOK, THAT WRITTEN RECORD OF THE INVESTIGATION YOUR APARTMENT RANSACKING HADN'T TURNED UP. FINALLY YOU LURED ME HERE, WHERE YOU KEPT ME BUSY, WHILE HARTOG STOLE THE BOOK... YOU PRETENDED TO PURSUE HIM, COMING BACK WITH A SPECIFIC DESCRIPTION OF A CAR, AND NO LICENSE NUMBER.

I NOTICE YOU'VE STOPPED DENYING ANY OF THIS.

WELL, DO IT. GET IT THE HELL OVER WITH.

ALL RIGHT.

WHAT ARE YOU DOING?

CALLING THE COPS. THE REAL COPS.

YOU'RE GOING TO PRISON, CHICK.

PRISON? BUT —

LOTS OF YOUR FRIENDS, THERE — PEOPLE YOU SENT UP. THEY'LL RAPE YOU. THEY'LL KILL YOU. IT'LL BE FUN.

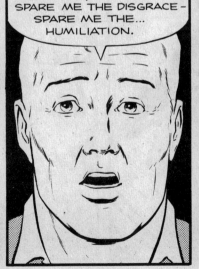

SHOOT ME, MICHAEL! SPARE ME THE DISGRACE — SPARE ME THE... HUMILIATION.

NO.

15

WELL, MIKE — IT'S OVER. YOUR KILLER AWAITS TRIAL, AND ALMOST CERTAIN DEATH. AND I CAN FACE TOMORROW.

OH — MS. TREE — I HOPE YOU DON'T MIND RUNNING INTO US AGAIN.

NO. NOT AT ALL.

I'M WORRIED ABOUT MIKE JR. HE HASN'T CRIED YET. HE LIKES YOU — WOULD YOU...?

SURE.

MIKE — IT'S ALL RIGHT. YOU MISS HIM. SO DO I. IT'S ALL RIGHT TO CRY.

THE END

—FOR MICKEY—

DEATH DO US PART

introduction by Terry Beatty

When Max Collins asked me if I could handle the job of drawing a realistic and gritty detective feature for Dean Mullaney's ECLIPSE MAGAZINE, I did what any self-respecting young cartoonist would do - I lied. You see, in 1980 (when we started working on MS. TREE), I was convinced I was going to make my mark on the world as a **funny** cartoonist, and had much more practice at drawing big feet and funny noses than I had at delineating handguns and trenchcoats. But no one was offering me the chance to do big feet and funny nose comics - what was being offered was MS. TREE. I started learning how to draw handguns and trenchcoats.

I stumbled through I, FOR AN EYE, learning as I went. It shows. Though there are bits and pieces of art in the early chapters that I am proud of, on the whole, I tend to cringe a bit when I look through them. Thank goodness Max's script and our lead character are so strong that they carry me in my weaker moments. I am also thankful that my attitude is such that I insist that each drawing I do be better than the last. I think if you'll compare the early chapters of I, FOR AN EYE with the later chapters of DEATH DO US PART, you'll see a marked improvement in my drawing. You'll also note a shift in style along with the improved drawing - a shift toward a **more** realistic and gritty approach than we began with - a natural shift, dictated by the needs of the story, not by any conscious decision on our part.

Max and I claim to be in charge of Ms. Tree's life, but the more we work with the character, the more we realize she has a life of her own. We tend not to **plan** MS. TREE stories - they just sort of happen on their own - events from the previous stories rolling over us like a big ball and taking us with them. We didn't intend for the death of Mike Tree to have such a lasting effect in the MS. TREE stories, but it **has.** Neither did we intend for Ms. Tree to carry on such a vendetta against the mob (see THE COLD DISH, our third MS. TREE serial - to be found in issues #4-8 of the MS. TREE comic book...or if you're the patient type, the second volume of THE FILES OF MS. TREE), but she has. And although that means we are sometimes faced with a surprise or two, we're glad our lovely detective gives us so much in the way of

direction -- it means we're not just pushing words and pictures around on paper -- we're telling honest-to-goodness **stories** about an honest-to-goodness character.

And Ms. Tree isn't the only character we have to deal with in these stories - we've got a full supporting cast whose surfaces we've only begun to scratch (see how much more full a character Dan Green is in DEATH DO US PART than he is in I, FOR AN EYE). Roger, Effie, Rafe Valer and (Brrrrr...) Dominic Muerta are characters whose potential is only hinted at in these two stories. We have much more to say about all of them, and I suggest you follow the monthly MS. TREE comic book to see what paths **they** lead us down.

You might notice that the version of the first chapter of DEATH DO US PART that appears here is practically smothered with grey tones. Though this is the way it was originally drawn, it never (until now) appeared in print this way. This was the first MS. TREE chapter to be printed in color (in MS. TREE'S THRILLING DETECTIVE ADVENTURES #1), but it was originally prepared for black and white publication in a proposed companion publication to ECLIPSE MAGAZINE. The magazine was to be called THRILLING DETECTIVE ADVENTURES (Max and I wanted to call it NOIR, but never mind) and would feature MS. TREE in the lead, with other detective and crime tales backing her up. Additionally, the magazine would feature columns and articles by top names in the mystery field (including Bob Randisi, who in real life is not a hitman or a victim of Ms. Tree's vigilante tactics, as he is in I, FOR AN EYE). We had hoped to lure some of the still-working EC artists (especially Johnny Craig) into our pages -- we had also arranged for Bill Griffith (of ZIPPY THE PINHEAD fame) to do special ZIPPY THE DETECTIVE strips for us. The magazine would have been a hard-boiled fan's delight. But it never happened. What did happen was a full-color comic book with the too-long title, MS. TREE'S THRILLING DETECTIVE ADVENTURES. So the grey tones were removed, color was added, we said goodbye to our dream of seeing new EC style suspense stories and Griffy's pinhead private eye, and the rest is, as Joseph E. Levine (or Tom

Snyder) would say, history.

In addition to presenting this chapter in its original form, we are also including in this volume the first promotional drawing of Ms. Tree - a drawing that has never before seen print without editorial tampering. You'll also find the cover art for the first and third issues of MS. TREE'S THRILLING ETC. ETC. AND SO FORTH. The first cover appears here sans copy because, damnit, I drew all those bricks and wanted somebody to see them. The third cover is included because the original printers (World Color Press) dropped out most of the detail in the drawing and, damnit, I drew all those lines and wanted somebody to see them. You can find the second cover, and indeed the first and third, in color on the back cover of this volume. They are joined by Paul Gulacy's gorgeous cover painting for ECLIPSE #6 (the nicest MS. TREE illo to date **would** have to be by another artist!). And while I'm discussing presenting things in their original form, I should mention that, despite the urge to go through these pages and touch-up and re-draw certain panels, I'm allowing all the art in this book to be printed in its original form (even that one panel in which ... aw, why should I point out **my** mistakes). I'll pause while all the purists say thanks.

And now a word for the completeists in the audience. This volume contains all the **MS. TREE** material from ECLIPSE MAGAZINE #1-6 and the first three issues of MS. TREE'S YOU-KNOW-WHAT. What it does not contain are the MIKE MIST strips and THE SCYTHE from the color comic. If you want to see those Collins/Beatty MINUTE MIST-ERIES: or the Dean Mullaney/Ellis Goodson strip, you'll have to pick up the back issues - ditto for the Frank Miller (and Mike Grell) FAMOUS DETECTIVE PIN-UPS).

What **is** in THE FILES OF MS. TREE that can be found nowhere else (in addition to the new cover and these rambling introductions) is a MS. TREE short story called RED LIGHT, written by Max Collins and illustrated by yours truly. This is the first time Ms. Tree has been committed to prose, and we think you'll find it...well, you'll find it on the pages directly following DEATH DO US PART.

I've often been asked what kind of working relationship Max Collins and I have... here it is - it's just like THE HONEYMOONERS. Max is Ralph Kramden, I'm Ed Norton, Max's wife Barb is the long-suffering Alice, and Trixie - well, auditions are still being held for that part.

I've rambled on long enough. You're probably anxious to read DEATH DO US PART and RED LIGHT, and I've got a comic book to draw. Hey Ralph! You got a new script for me yet?

Terry Beatty
April 14, 1984

COVER FOR ISSUE #1.

COVER ART FOR "MS. TREE'S THRILLING DETECTIVE ADVENTURES" #3

DEATH DO US PART

Ms. TREE

"DEATH DO US PART"

by Max Collins and Terry Beatty

Chapter One — THE WOMAN in THE BLACK BIKINI

©1982 Collins and Beatty

I WAS ALONE ON THE BEACH. WHITE SAND. GREEN PINES.

1

THE SUN IS OUT — SHINING BRIGHTLY — SHIMMERING ON THE WATER —

WHY, THEN, AM I SO COLD?

A COUPLE STROLLS ONTO THE BEACH — YOUNG, IN LOVE — THE BOY RESEMBLES MY OLD HIGH SCHOOL FLAME, BILLY — THE GIRL'S FACE I CAN'T MAKE OUT —

SUDDENLY A CHILD JOINS THEM — HE'S THEIR SON, IT WOULD SEEM — FUNNY, THEY SEEM TOO YOUNG TO HAVE A CHILD —

LOOK, MOMMY! MOMMY, LOOK!

THE COUPLE DOESN'T SEE THE FORM RISING FROM THE WATER —

I SEE HIM RETREAT TO THE SAFETY OF THE SEA —

STOP! STOP!

AND I TAKE PURSUIT...

2

IT'S CHICK! CHICK STEELE!

I SCRATCH HIS FACE —

AND THE SKIN COMES OFF — THE FLESH FALLS AWAY —

THEN HE'S GONE —

ON THE BEACH, THE BOY IS FRIGHTENED, CONFUSED — I WANT TO CONSOLE HIM —

HE RUNS FROM ME.

THEN I NOTICE THE FACE OF THE DEAD WOMAN —

MY FACE!

I BEND TO HER, BUT A FIGURE IS APPROACHING BEHIND ME —

BUT BEFORE I CAN TURN AND LOOK —

3

I WAKE.

YOU'VE HAD THIS DREAM BEFORE, MS. TREE — THOUGH THERE ARE A FEW VARIANTS, THIS TIME.

"BUT THE BASIC INTERPRETATION REMAINS THE SAME — THE COUPLE REPRESENTS YOU AND YOUR HUSBAND, MIKE TREE —"

YOU HAVE SUBSTITUTED THE IDEALIZED LOVE REPRESENTED BY YOUR FIRST HIGH SCHOOL LOVE — BUT THE BOY IS YOUR HUSBAND, JUST AS YOU ARE THE GIRL.

"THE DANGER INHERENT IN THE SITUATION REFLECTS THE NATURE OF YOUR HUSBAND'S BUSINESS —

"WHICH YOU, OF COURSE, HAVE INHERITED."

"YOU ARE RE-LIVING THE TRAUMA OF HIS DEATH, THAT COLD RAINY NIGHT — IN THE DREAM THE SUN SHINES, BUT YOU ARE COLD, AND WATER IS NEARBY..."

"THIS IS MADE OBVIOUS BY THE CONFRONTATION WITH THE FROGMAN — WHO, AS IN LIFE, WAS THE ONE RESPONSIBLE FOR YOUR HUSBAND'S MURDER: HIS FORMER PARTNER FROM HIS POLICE DAYS, CHICK STEELE."

"THE CHILD IS THE CHILD YOU WERE DENIED — THE CHILD YOU NEVER HAD WITH MIKE — THE CHILD HE DID HAVE WITH HIS FIRST WIFE."

4

BUT WHAT OF THE NEW ELEMENT, DR. KASSEL? THE MAN WHO APPROACHES AS I WAKE — ?

THIS IS YOUR FIRST SESSION SINCE THE HOLIDAY I SUGGESTED YOU TAKE, MS. TREE... PERHAPS THE ANSWER LIES IN THESE PAST WEEKS —

I'M SURE OF IT, DOCTOR — IM SURE OF IT —

THE AFTERMATH OF MIKE'S MURDER — THE MURDER ITSELF, THEN THE SOLVING OF IT — WAS AN ANTICLIMAX... I TRIED TO GO BACK TO WORK —

MS. TREE — ARE YOU ALL RIGHT?

SURE, EFFIE —

BUT I WASN'T ALL RIGHT — I HAD INSOMNIA — TERRIBLE INSOMNIA — AND WHEN I COULD SLEEP, I HAD THE DREAM —

THE AGENCY BORED ME — EVERYTHING SEEMED ROUTINE, UNIMPORTANT; MY INTEREST WAS NEXT TO NIL...

GLAD TO HAVE YOU BACK, ROGER — GET DAN AND COME INTO MY OFFICE.

I DID, HOWEVER, HAVE OTHER PLANS.

I'M ASSIGNING ALL MY CASES TO YOU. IF YOU FEEL YOU NEED EXTRA HELP, WE'LL TAKE ON MORE OPERATIVES. OTHERWISE, HANDLE THE WORKLOAD YOURSELVES.

5

THERE WAS THE USUAL OBJECTION FROM DAN GREEN —

LOOK, MS. TREE — MIKE'S MURDER IS OLD NEWS; YOU SOLVED IT. SHOWED THE WORLD YOU'RE A REAL DETECTIVE — NOW, LET'S GET BACK TO NORMAL —

NORMAL? NORMAL WOULD BE MIKE IN THIS CHAIR. NORMAL DOESN'T EVEN EXIST ANYMORE.

HEY... I'M SORRY, MS. TREE... I...

COME ON, KID — LET'S GET TO WORK.

I BEGAN TO HAUNT THE LIBRARY — LOOKING FOR ANSWERS ON MICROFILM —

CHICK STEELE, CROOKED COP WITH MOB TIES, HAD HAD MY HUSBAND KILLED; CHICK WAS AWAITING TRIAL.

LT. CHARLES "CHICK" STEELE HEADS ORGANIZED CRIME PROBE
activities of local businesses and banks. links created

BUT THE MOB WAS STILL AT LARGE —

DA DROPS MUERTA CASE

INSUFFICIENT EVIDENCE

MOB PROBE ENDS

THE MOB — THE MOB — JUST A COUPLE OF WORDS. I HAD TO TURN IT INTO NAMES — AND I HAD TO TURN THE NAMES INTO PEOPLE.

AND IT ALL SEEMED TO BOIL DOWN TO ONE MAN: DOMINIC MUERTA, A SELF-MADE MAN WHOSE TRUCKING COMPANY WAS A LEGITIMATE BUSINESS THAT WAS ONLY THE TIP OF AN ICEBERG THAT, BENEATH THE WATER'S SURFACE, WAS DARK, RANK, MISSHAPEN —

EFFORTS TO INDICT MUERTA FAIL

6

THERE WAS A MAN ON THE FORCE MIKE HAD TRUSTED — SGT. RAFE VALER; THEY'D MOVED HIM UP INTO CHICK'S OLD OFFICE —

MUERTA CAN'T BE TOUCHED, MICHAEL.

HE'S TOO WELL INSULATED — HE NEVER GIVES AN ORDER WITHOUT GOING THROUGH THREE INTERMEDIARIES — HE'S NEVER DIRECTLY INVOLVED IN THE CRIMINAL ACTS HE CONDUCTS —

PRIMARILY DRUG TRAFFICKING — HIS TRUCKING FIRM COULD COME IN HANDY, THERE. I WANT HIM RAFE. HE'S THE MAN CHICK WAS COVERING UP FOR —

GO BACK TO WORK, MICHAEL — FORGET THIS!

NO! NO! SOMEONE HAS TO DO SOMETHING! I HAVE TO DO SOMETHING...

LET THE POLICE DO THEIR JOB —

LIKE CHICK?

LADY, WE'RE NOT ALL IN BED WITH THE MOB — I'M NO CHICK STEELE!

I KNOW. I'M SORRY, RAFE.

I... I DON'T KNOW WHAT'S WRONG WITH ME...

I WENT BACK TO THE OFFICE HOPING TO GET AHOLD OF MYSELF —

MS. TREE, THIS IS DIANE LATIMER...

NOT NOW!

MS. TREE — MICHAEL... DIANE'S HERE ABOUT THE RECEPTIONIST'S POSITION — YOU SAW HER APPLICATION — SAID YOU WANTED TO INTERVIEW HER YOURSELF...

WHAT'S WRONG?

I HAVEN'T BEEN SLEEPING... MY FUSE IS SHORTER THAN A TWO-YEAR-OLD'S ATTENTION SPAN...

DON'T TAKE THIS WRONG — PLEASE. BUT WE'RE ALL A LITTLE WORRIED ABOUT YOU, MICHAEL. YOU'VE GOT TO SEEK HELP —

AND THAT'S WHAT FINALLY BROUGHT ME HERE, DOCTOR —

AND YOU ADVISED I TAKE A VACATION —

GET AWAY FROM IT ALL... TWO WEEKS AT PINE BEACH RESORT — BUT SOMEONE ELSE WAS ALREADY THERE, DOCTOR... SOMEONE WHO WASN'T ON VACATION...

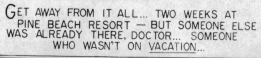

8

Ms. TREE

"DEATH DO US PART"

by Max Collins and Terry Beatty

Chapter Two

SECOND HONEYMOON

PINE BEACH RESORT... JUST WHAT THE DOCTOR ORDERED...

©1982 Collins and Beatty

IT'S BEAUTIFUL — HASN'T CHANGED SINCE I WAS A KID!

THAT'S RIGHT! YOUR FOLKS USED TO COME HERE ALL THE TIME...

A COUPLE OF KIDS ON THEIR HONEYMOON... I HAD A RUSH OF SOME EMOTION I CAN'T NAME... A BITTERSWEET SENSATION.

THEY EVEN HONEYMOONED HERE...

PARKING
MAIN LO
LAKE

1

WAS THAT RESERVATION IN THE MAIN LODGE, OR...

PRIVATE CABIN. IT'S MICHAEL TREE.

AH, YES — BUT IT'S A RESERVATION FOR ONE —

SO?

WELL — IS "MICHAEL TREE" A... FRIEND OF YOURS? YOUR... HUSBAND PERHAPS?

I'M MICHAEL TREE —

MIKE HAD JOKED ABOUT IT AT THE MOTEL THAT NIGHT —

YOUR LAST NAME'S TREE, TOO, NOW, YOU KNOW — THAT MAKES US BOTH MICHAEL TREE —

I'M SORRY — I DIDN'T MEAN TO BE RUDE.

THAT'S OKAY. MICHAEL'S AN UNUSUAL NAME FOR A WOMAN.

I'D JOKED, TOO —

YOU'LL JUST HAVE TO STICK TO "MIKE" — MICHAEL'S MINE.

YOU BET HE IS.

MS. TREE? YOUR KEY...?

OH — THANK YOU...

2

"IT'S A VERY NICE CABIN, NEAR THE BEACH — ONE OF OUR HONEYMOON CABINS, ACTUALLY..."

I WOULD'VE LOVED TO COME HERE WITH YOU, MIKE — BUT I THINK COMING HERE ALONE WAS A MISTAKE...

BUT I WAS STILL THINKING ABOUT YOUR ADVICE, DOCTOR... "GET IN THE SWIM OF IT," YOU SAID — SO I TOOK YOU LITERALLY —

THE CABIN NEXT DOOR WAS FAR ENOUGH FROM MINE TO INSURE PRIVACY — BUT NOT SO FAR THAT I COULDN'T GET THE IDEA —

IT WAS A HONEYMOON CABIN, ALL RIGHT.

AND NOW THE BITTER PART OF THAT BITTERSWEET SENSATION HAD FLOWN —

IT WAS SWEET — ONLY SWEET — TO SEE THEM LOVE EACH OTHER LIKE THAT.

I WISHED IT WAS MIKE AND ME —

BUT I COULD ACCEPT THAT IT WASN'T.

AND THEN I STEPPED ONTO THE BEACH —

3

IT WAS THE BEACH IN MY DREAM! WHITE SAND, GREEN PINES —

I FELT DIZZY —

ARE YOU ALL RIGHT?

Y-YES

I THOUGHT YOU WERE GOING TO FAINT OR SOMETHING, FOR A WHILE THERE —

SO DID I.

CAN I GET YOU SOMETHING? I CAN RUN BACK TO THE LODGE FOR A DRINK FOR YOU — OR WHATEVER...

NO — YOU'RE VERY KIND, THOUGH. WHY DON'T YOU JOIN ME? I... I COULD USE SOME COMPANY.

THAT'S THE BEST OFFER I'VE HAD IN TWO WEEKS.

YOU'VE BEEN HERE THAT LONG?

YEAH — CAME FOR THE PEACE AND QUIET — THEN GOT BORED... AND FOUND OUT THIS PLACE IS NO "SINGLES" HAVEN.

WELL, I'M SINGLE...

4

THAT'S NICE TO HEAR. HOW'D YOU LAND A CABIN IN THIS HONEYMOONERS' GHETTO?

GOD, I SUPPOSE.

GOD?

YEAH — GOD'S GOT NO SENSE OF HUMOR, BUT IRONY? THAT HE CREATED ON THE 7TH DAY.

YOU'RE AN INTERESTING LADY

MY NAME'S MICHAEL TREE. WHAT'S YOURS?

PATRICK RUSHING WAS HIS NAME. AND HE WAS A WRITER — A NOVELIST.

HAVE I READ ANYTHING YOU EVER WROTE?

I DOUBT IT. YOU DON'T LOOK LIKE THE BLOOD-AND-GUTS TYPE, MICHAEL.

OH?

MY PEN-NAME'S DEREK RODD — I WRITE A PULP CRIME SERIES... YOU KNOW, PAPERBACKS.

SURE — THE "HITMAN" BOOKS!

THAT'S RIGHT. DON'T TELL ME...

MY LATE HUSBAND USED TO READ 'EM. I NEVER GOT PAST THE GARISH COVERS.

WELL, YOU KNOW WHAT THEY SAY ABOUT A BOOK...

5

SO YOU'RE A WIDOW. RETIRED AND WEALTHY? I COULD *USE* A PATRON...

I'M A BUSINESS-WOMAN.

WHAT BUSINESS?

LET'S JUST SAY YOU DON'T KNOW IT, BUT YOU'RE DOING RESEARCH RIGHT NOW.

A PRIVATE EYE? YOU'RE KIDDIN' ME!

WANT TO SEE MY GUN?

DID YOU BRING IT ALONG?

SURE - IT'S IN IN MY CABIN - I'LL SHOW YOU MINE IF...

I BELIEVE THIS *IS* A HONEYMOON COTTAGE --

HEY - I WAS JUST MAKIN' A JOKE - YOU... WHY ARE YOU... CRYING?

6

SO I FINALLY TOLD HIM. TOLD HIM ABOUT MIKE'S MURDER, ON OUR HONEYMOON NIGHT.

AND YOU SOLVED HIS MURDER. I NEVER CAME UP WITH A PLOT THAT GOOD.

YOU CAN HAVE IT. MAYBE IT'LL READ BETTER THAN IT LIVED.

DO YOU BELIEVE IN PRECOGNITION?

I DON'T KNOW. WHY?

I'VE SEEN THIS BEACH BEFORE. IN A DREAM.

A DREAM?

A NIGHTMARE. BUT YOU KNOW SOMETHING FUNNY...

LAST NIGHT — WHEN I WAS WITH YOU — I DIDN'T HAVE THE DREAM. FIRST TIME IN WEEKS —

SEE? I'M GOOD FOR YOU.

AND HE WAS, TOO. HE WAS BETTER MEDICINE THAN ANY DOCTOR COULD PRESCRIBE — NO OFFENSE, DR. KASSEL...

SO I CAME HERE TO RELAX — BUT BROUGHT MY TYPEWRITER JUST THE SAME.

7

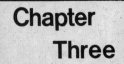

Ms. TREE

"DEATH DO US PART"

by **Max Collins** and **Terry Beatty**

Chapter Three

ONE LONELY NIGHTMARE

PINE BEACH RESORT WAS SUPPOSED TO BE RESTFUL — IT MIGHT HELP ME TO ESCAPE THE MEMORY OF MY HUSBAND'S MURDER, ON OUR HONEYMOON NIGHT, MONTHS AGO —

NO!

©1982 Collins and Beatty

IT WAS AS IF THAT NIGHTMARE I'D BEEN HAVING HAD COME SUDDENLY TRUE —

NOT LITERALLY, MS. TREE.

NO, BUT IT PREFIGURED THE REALITY — IN MY RECURRING DREAM I'D SEEN A YOUNG COUPLE ON A BEACH KILLED; HERE, THEY'D DIED IN BED, IN THEIR HONEYMOON CABIN...

BASTARD!

I HAD SEEN THE RED-HAIRED GUNMAN FLEEING THE CABIN — I SHOULD'VE TAKEN IMMEDIATE PURSUIT, BUT FELT COMPELLED TO CHECK INSIDE THE CABIN FIRST...

WHICH WAY DID HE GO, PATRICK!

OH MY GOD...

PATRICK!

UHHH...

SORRY — HE WENT THAT-AWAY... TOWARD THE PARKING LOT.

THERE WAS NO ATTENDANT IN THE LOT... BUT SOME PEOPLE HAD JUST PULLED IN —

DID ANYONE PASS YOU, GOING OUT AS YOU CAME IN?

YEAH — SOMEBODY IN A BLUE BUICK.

WHAT DID HE LOOK LIKE!

TAKE IT EASY, LADY! I COULDN'T EVEN SEE IF IT WAS A "HE"...

BY THE TIME I COULD'VE GOTTEN BACK TO MY CABIN, AND GOT MY OWN CAR KEYS, THE BLUE BUICK WOULD BE EVEN LONGER GONE THAN IT ALREADY WAS... PURSUIT WAS WISHFUL THINKING.

2

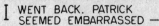

I WENT BACK. PATRICK SEEMED EMBARRASSED —

NICE BEHAVIOR, FOR THE AUTHOR OF MACHO PAPER-BACKS — PUKING AT THE SIGHT OF BLOOD...

IT'S JUST... I'VE WRITTEN ABOUT DEATH, BUT ONLY AS A SILLY PULP FANTASY. THIS IS THE FIRST TIME I...

EVER REALLY HAD TO FACE IT?

YEAH.

WELL, IT DOESN'T GET EASIER THE SECOND TIME. COME ON — LET'S GET THE MANAGER OR SOMEBODY...

SHOTGUN FIRE SHATTERING THE SILENCE OF THE SUMMER NIGHT HAD ATTRACTED NO ONE'S ATTENTION BUT OURS — THE HONEY-MOON CABIN WAS ONE OF THREE NEAR THE BEACH FAR ENOUGH AWAY FROM THE MAIN LODGE TO ASSURE PRIVACY.

THIS IS TERRIBLE!

RIGHT.

BOTH PATRICK AND I SPENT HOURS WITH THE POLICE. CAPTAIN SAM MEYERS, OF THE STATE BUREAU OF CRIMINAL INVESTIGATION, WAS IN CHARGE —

LOOKS LIKE THE KILLER HAD THE THIRD OF THESE ISOLATED CABINS.

WE WERE IN MY CABIN AT THE MOMENT —

WE'RE GOING OVER HIS CABIN NOW, BUT WE WON'T FIND ANYTHING — THE GUY'S OBVIOUSLY A PRO.

MIND IF I HAVE A LOOK?

NOT AT ALL, MS. TREE — WE'RE LUCKY TO HAVE A TRAINED OBSERVER LIKE YOU ON THE SCENE.

FOR ALL THE GOOD IT DID THOSE KIDS.

3

IN THE WASTE BASKET IN THE BATHROOM, LODGED BETWEEN THE PAPER LINER AND THE BASKET ITSELF, I FOUND SOMETHING —

SMELLS LIKE ETHER...

SPIRIT GUM — IT'S HOW ACTORS KEEP FAKE FACIAL HAIR ON.

"THAT MAKES THE SKETCH OUR ARTIST'S WORKING UP DAMN NEAR WORTHLESS..."

YOUR ARTIST SHOULD BE ABLE TO DO A CLEAN-SHAVEN VERSION THAT'LL BE OF SOME USE...

WE'VE TAKEN THE PICTURES, CAPTAIN — AND THE MEDICAL EXAMINER'S DONE. SHOULD WE...?

YEAH. LET'S GET 'EM LOADED UP.

NOT MY IDEA OF A HONEYMOON.

WHO WERE THEY, MEYER? WHY WOULD ANYBODY KILL A YOUNG COUPLE LIKE THAT?

I TRUST THIS IS PURE CURIOSITY, ON YOUR PART — I WASN'T KIDDING WHEN I SAID I WAS GLAD YOU WERE ON THE SCENE... AN INVESTIGATOR MAKES A HELL OF A GOOD WITNESS.

BUT I KNOW ABOUT YOU, LADY. I READ THE PAPERS.

AND YOU CAN HANDLE YOUR OWN INVESTIGATION, THANKS – RIGHT?

RIGHT. ANYWAY, THE GIRL'S FAMILY NAME WAS MUERTA...

4

MUERTA? YOU MEAN TO SAY...

HER UNCLE IS DOMINIC MUERTA. THE MOB GUY. YES. NOW, <u>LEAVE IT ALONE</u>, MS. TREE.

DOMINIC MUERTA — THE MOB BOSS WHO, INDIRECTLY AT LEAST, PLAYED A ROLE IN MY HUSBAND MIKE TREE'S DEATH...

LOOK — MUERTA'S BROTHER APPARENTLY ISN'T "CONNECTED" ...HE'S IN THE ART GALLERY BUSINESS — SEEMS TO BE STRAIGHT.

BUT THAT WAS A PRO KILL TONIGHT — AND A VICIOUS ONE, AT THAT. IT'S GOT MOB WRITTEN ALL OVER IT — IN BLOOD.

MAYBE SO. BUT THE GROOM WAS JUST SOME KID FROM FLORIDA SHE MET AT COLLEGE IN THE CITY. NAMED ASKAM. AND THAT'S ALL WE KNOW SO FAR...

I WALKED TO THE BEACH — THE BEACH THAT SO RESEMBLED THE BEACH IN MY DREAM — A RECURRING DREAM IN WHICH THE MAN <u>DIRECTLY</u> RESPONSIBLE FOR MIKE'S MURDER KILLED A YOUNG COUPLE —

THOUGHT I'D FIND YOU HERE. DISAPPOINTED IN ME?

PATRICK! OF COURSE NOT... YOU'RE FINISHED WITH THE POLICE?

5

YES, BUT WE'LL BOTH BE HEARING FROM THEM AGAIN. MICHAEL, I'M SO EMBARRASSED — I FELL APART. HOW CAN YOU BE SO STRONG?

BECAUSE IF YOU'RE WEAK, YOU'RE DEAD... IN MY BUSINESS, ANYWAY.

YOUR HUSBAND WAS STRONG. IT DIDN'T SAVE HIM.

YOU CAN ALWAYS GET HIT BY A TRUCK, PATRICK —

OR A FALLING BEAM.

WHAT DO YOU MEAN?

"THAT'S A DASHIELL HAMMETT REFERENCE. I'M A MYSTERY WRITER, REMEMBER? HAMMETT SAW THE UNIVERSE AS A PLACE WHERE BEAMS WERE CONSTANTLY FALLING — BUT IT HELPS IF YOU KNOW THEY'RE FALLING."

I'D AGREE WITH THAT.

FORGIVE ME FOR NOT BEING STRONGER?

BEING CALLOUS ABOUT DEATH AND VIOLENCE ISN'T "STRENGTH," PATRICK — YOUR REATION TONIGHT WAS ONLY HUMAN...

6

THOSE POOR KIDS... I'D LIKE TO...

DO SOMETHING ABOUT IT? SO WOULD I. SO _AM_ I.

DON'T TELL ME YOU'RE GOING TO TRACK DOWN THAT RED-HEADED KILLER —

JUST LIKE IN THE MYSTERY BOOKS, PATRICK — ONLY I DOUBT HE WAS A REAL REDHEAD.

I TOLD HIM ABOUT THE EMPTY BOTTLE OF SPIRIT GUM —

FINDING HIM WILL ONLY BE THE FIRST STEP — HE WAS AN EMPLOYEE. I WANT HIS EMPLOYER.

AND WHAT WILL YOU DO ABOUT IT?

KILL THE SON OF A BITCH.

THAT WAS OUR LAST NIGHT AT THE LODGE TOGETHER. BUT WE MADE A DATE TO SEE EACH OTHER LATER THAT WEEK, IN THE CITY...

PATRICK WORKED UPSTATE IN WHAT HE DESCRIBED AS A "SECLUDED STUDIO RETREAT"; BUT HE GOT INTO THE CITY OFTEN, ON PUBLISHING BUSINESS —

WISH THIS IDYL HADN'T TAKEN SUCH A NASTY TURN...

WE'LL DO BETTER NEXT TIME.

7

THEY WEREN'T EXPECTING ME BACK AT THE OFFICE THAT AFTERNOON...

MS. TREE —

HELLO. DO I KNOW YOU?

Michael Tree
president

I TOOK THE LIBERTY OF HIRING HER. I HEARD THE NEWS TODAY —

OH BOY. CAN'T YOU EVEN STAY OUT OF TROUBLE ON VACATION?

I CALLED EFFIE, DAN GREEN AND ROGER FREEMONT IN, TO ANNOUNCE MY INTENTIONS.

I'M GOING TO INVESTIGATE THE MURDER OF THESE KIDS.

WHY?

TWO REASONS: THE FIRST IS MUERTA; THE SECOND IS NOBODY'S GODDAMN BUSINESS BUT MINE.

A COUPLE KILLED ON THEIR HONEYMOON — RIGHT UNDER YOUR NOSE. YEAH, I CAN SEE IT. GO GET 'EM, MS. TREE —

MS. TREE — THERE'S SOMEONE OUT HERE TO SEE YOU —

HE SAYS HIS NAME IS MUERTA.

8

Ms. TREE

"DEATH DO US PART"
by Max Collins and Terry Beatty

Chapter Four

GOING DOWN

©1983 Max Collins and Terry Beatty

I DIDN'T KNOW IT AT THE TIME...

BUT SOMEWHERE WITHIN MY BUILDING...

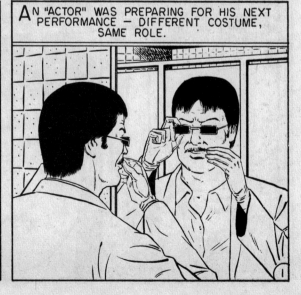

AN "ACTOR" WAS PREPARING FOR HIS NEXT PERFORMANCE — DIFFERENT COSTUME, SAME ROLE.

1

YOU'RE NOT DOMINIC MUERTA!

WAS I ANNOUNCED AS SUCH? I'M *FRANCESCO* MUERTA — DOMINIC IS MY BROTHER.

EXCUSE MY... PRESUMPTIVENESS AND RUDENESS. DO SIT DOWN, MR. MUERTA. AND PLEASE ACCEPT MY SINCERE SYMPATHY FOR YOUR DAUGHTER'S... DEATH.

MY DAUGHTER'S *MURDER*, RATHER. I WISH TO THANK YOU FOR YOUR HELPFULNESS AT THE SCENE. CAPTAIN MEYERS, IN OUR TELEPHONE CONVERSATION, SPOKE FLATTERINGLY OF YOU. MAY I SMOKE?

CERTAINLY. BUT IF YOU'VE COME FOR ANY INFORMATION THAT I MIGHT HAVE NEGLECTED TO TELL THE CAPTAIN I'M AFRAID...

THAT'S NOT WHY I'VE COME, MS. TREE. I'M SURE YOU DID YOUR CIVIC DUTY, LAST NIGHT, AND MORE.

WHY *ARE* YOU HERE, MR. MUERTA?

TO HIRE YOU TO FIND MY DAUGHTER'S KILLER.

2

MR. MUERTA — I ADMIT HAVING A CERTAIN PERSONAL INTEREST IN THIS CASE, HAVING BEEN ON THE SCENE...

AND HAVING SURVIVED A VIOLENT HONEYMOON OF YOUR OWN — IF YOU'LL FORGIVE MY MENTIONING WHAT IS I'M SURE A SENSITIVE SUBJECT.

WHAT MAKES YOU THINK CAPTAIN MEYERS WON'T FIND THE KILLER HIMSELF?

"WE BOTH KNOW THAT THE MAN TECHNICALLY RESPONSIBLE IS A PROFESSIONAL," FRANCESCO MUERTA SAID.

I WANT HIM, OF COURSE — BUT I WANT WHOEVER HIRED HIM MORE. CAPTAIN MEYERS, GOOD MAN THOUGH HE SEEMS TO BE, COULD NEVER GET THAT FAR.

BECAUSE THIS IS A MOB KILLING? IS THAT THE LINE YOU WANT ME TO READ BETWEEN?

I'M NOT INVOLVED WITH THE MOB, MS. TREE. BUT MY BROTHER IS. I FEAR MY DAUGHTER MAY BE AN INNOCENT BYSTANDER MADE GUILTY BY BLOOD — MUERTA BLOOD.

THEN WHY NOT ASK YOUR BROTHER TO FIND OUT WHO'S RESPONSIBLE FOR HER MURDER?

BECAUSE HE MAY BE RESPONSIBLE.

③

THIS IS A CHECK FOR $5000 — A RETAINER —

A GENEROUS RETAINER —

WE'LL TALK MORE TOMORROW — I WILL TELL YOU THINGS I CANNOT TELL CAPTAIN MEYERS.

ANOTHER REASON WHY YOU WANT YOUR OWN DETECTIVE INVESTIGATING —

YES. THIS IS A FAMILY MATTER...

YOU DO REALIZE THAT I'D LIKE NOTHING BETTER THAN TO FIND A REASON TO KILL YOUR GODDAMN BROTHER.

YOU ALREADY HAVE A REASON, MS. TREE. WHAT YOU'RE LOOKING FOR, I BELIEVE, IS AN EXCUSE.

MAYBE SO. DO YOU STILL WANT ME ON RETAINER, KNOWING THAT?

PERHAPS THAT IS WHY I WANT YOU ON RETAINER, MY DEAR.

AND NOW I HAVE THE UNPLEASANT DUTY OF GOING TO PINE BEACH TO IDENTIFY "THE BODY." "THE BODY" — WHICH USED TO BE MY DAUGHTER... MY ONLY CHILD...

FORGIVE ME. TOMORROW MORNING AT MY GALLERY? SHALL WE SAY NINE?

NINE IT IS.

4

HERE'S A CHECK TO BANK, EFFIE — AND DRAW UP OUR STANDARD CONTRACT FOR THE SIGNATOR...

DO YOU WANT THAT CONTRACT YET TODAY, MS. TREE?

I GUESS IT IS QUITTING TIME, AT THAT — FIRST THING IN THE MORNING'LL BE FINE, EFFIE.

WASN'T THAT THE MUERTA GIRL'S OLD MAN? DON'T TELL ME YOU GOT HIM TO UNDERWRITE YOUR LATEST CRUSADE —

HOW 'BOUT GRABBING SOME SUPPER WITH US, MS. TREE? YOU CAN FILL US IN...

SOUNDS LIKE THE MAIN COURSE IS CURIOSITY —

OKAY, OKAY — I'LL MEET YOU GUYS AT DIAMOND'S, IN HALF AN HOUR — I WANT TO GATHER UP SOME THINGS.

I'D BEEN KEEPING A CLIP FILE ON THE MOB — AS WELL AS PHOTOCOPIES FROM NEWSPAPER FILE MICROFILM...

I WANTED TO GO THROUGH 'EM THAT NIGHT, AT HOME, TO SEE IF FRANCESCO MUERTA'S NAME TURNED UP AT ALL —

AND I'D CHECK WITH SGT. VALER, TOO, TO SEE IF HE KNEW WHETHER THIS MUERTA REALLY WAS THE MOB VIRGIN HE CLAIMED TO BE.

STOP!
STOP...

THAT WAS WHEN I PASSED OUT.

7

SGT. RAFE VALER WAS THERE WHEN I WOKE UP –

YOU SCARED THOSE PEOPLE – THEY CALLED THE COPS, BUT NOBODY HAD THE NERVE TO TOUCH YOU.

DID THEY CHASE THE SON-OF-A-BITCH WHO DID THIS TO ME?

NO, THIS IS THE THIRD FLOOR – HE MUST'VE TAKEN THE STAIRS DOWN TO STREET LEVEL, AND BLENDED IN WITH THE RUSH HOUR CROWD.

DAMN!

WE BETTER GET YOU TO A MEDIC–

NO HOSPITALS! I'M FINE –

I WANT TO MEET WITH YOU AND CAPTAIN MEYERS OF THE B.C.I. SOMETIME TOMORROW. CAN YOU ARRANGE IT?

S-SURE.

IF YOU WANT A STATEMENT, I'LL GIVE IT TO YOU THEN –

EXIT

I WAS HALF AN HOUR LATE, BUT DAN AND ROGER WERE STILL WAITING FOR ME AT DIAMOND'S STEAK HOUSE–

MS. TREE!

YOU OUGHTA SEE THE OTHER GUY.

YOU WANT US TO GET YOU A RARE STEAK FOR THAT EYE?

NO THANKS – THINGS ARE GETTING BLOODY ENOUGH ALREADY. I THINK MY NEW CLIENT JUST TRIED TO HAVE ME KILLED...

8

Ms. TREE

"DEATH DO US PART"
by Max Collins and Terry Beatty

Chapter Five

© 1983 Max Collins and Terry Beatty

SOMEBODY TRIED TO KILL ME !

MS. TREE — THAT'S MOST DISTRESSING NEWS, CERTAINLY — BUT SURELY YOU DON'T THINK I...?

YOU — YOU COULD HAVE SET ME UP, YES... ASCERTAINED I WAS IN THE BUILDING — LEFT FOR YOUR PINE BEACH ALIBI —

WHY WOULD I DO SUCH A THING ?

BECAUSE YOU'RE A MUERTA...

BECAUSE YOU AND YOUR BROTHER DOMINIC KNOW I'M OUT TO GET HIM, ANY WAY I CAN — BECAUSE YOU ONLY PRETEND TO BE ALOOF FROM YOUR BROTHER AND HIS BUSINESS —

"YOUR BUSINESS — THIS ART GALLERY OF YOURS — IS A PERFECT FRONT FOR DRUG TRAFFICKING, AFTER ALL — LIKE YOUR BROTHER'S TRUCKING FIRM."

MUERT
GALLER

THIS LITTLE PIECE COMES FROM MEXICO, FOR EXAMPLE. GET MY DRIFT?

MS. TREE — PLEASE — COME TO MY OFFICE — SOME PRIVACY, PLEASE...

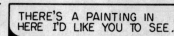

THERE'S A PAINTING IN HERE I'D LIKE YOU TO SEE.

I'VE SEEN ENOUGH OF THIS ERSATZ JACKSON POLLOCK BULLSHIT YOU CON YOUR PATRONS WITH.

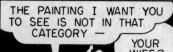

THE PAINTING I WANT YOU TO SEE IS NOT IN THAT CATEGORY —

YOUR WIFE?

"YES — DEAD SOME FIFTEEN YEARS, NOW. MY BROTHER, INDIRECTLY, WAS RESPONSIBLE. AS YOU CAN SEE, MY DAUGHTER WAS THE IMAGE OF HER MOTHER — TO HAVE LOST THEM BOTH..."

2

MS. TREE, THERE WAS A TIME WHEN I WAS INVOLVED IN MY BROTHER'S BUSINESS — THE PRESSURE OF IT KILLED MY WIFE. AND I WALKED AWAY FROM DOMINIC, AND HIS BLOOD MONEY.

BUT THIS BUSINESS — EXCUSE ME FOR SAYING SO — THIS BUSINESS OF YOURS WAS BUILT ON THAT BLOOD MONEY.

YES — AND I'M AFRAID IT'S COME BACK TO HAUNT ME — I'M AFRAID MY DAUGHTER MAY BE DEAD BECAUSE OF IT.

"YOU SEE," FRANCESCO MUERTA SAID, "HER FIANCE — OR I SHOULD SAY NEWLYWED HUSBAND — WAS AN ASKAM — AND THE ASKAMS ARE A FAMILY IN FLORIDA ONCE ALLIGNED WITH THE MUERTAS IN THE DRUG SMUGGLING TRADE."

THE ROX
TONITE!
the CAUCASIANS

IS JIMMY PLUGG AROUND?

SURE — HE'S ME. GOT SOMETHIN' IN MIND, BABE? I GOT A SOUND CHECK TO RUN.

I UNDERSTAND YOU'RE A FRIEND OF DAVE ASKAM'S?

YEAH. WE ROOMED AT COLLEGE AT MIAMI, 'FORE I SPLIT. WHY?

AND YOU'RE WORKING NOW AS A ROADIE WITH ROCK BANDS...

I'M A SOUND MAN, YEAH. WHAT'S THIS ABOUT? HOW DO YOU KNOW ABOUT ME AND DAVE? WHO ARE YOU, LADY?

3

FRANCESCO MUERTA TOLD ME YOU WERE BEST MAN AT THE WEDDING OF HIS DAUGHTER AND ASKAM, TWO DAYS AGO.

THAT'S RIGHT — THEY PLANNED IT FOR WHEN I HAD A GIG IN THE CITY, SO I WAS ABLE TO STAND UP WITH DAVE. SO?

YOU KNEW HIM PRETTY WELL, I TAKE IT.

LADY, WHO THE HELL ARE YOU... WHAT DO YOU MEAN, "KNEW"?

DIDN'T YOU KNOW HE WAS DEAD?

DEAD?

CHRIST, LADY — YOU MUST'VE TAKEN TACT LESSONS FROM JOHNNY ROTTEN —

SORRY. ASKAM AND HIS WIFE WERE MURDERED NIGHT BEFORE LAST. SHOTGUNNED.

JESUS! I THINK I'M GOING TO BE SICK —

WHAT CAN YOU TELL ME ABOUT DAVE AND HIS FAMILY?

THEY WERE TIGHT.

WAS DAVE GOING INTO THE FAMILY BUSINESS?

HEY, BABE — THIS IS GETTING A LITTLE HEAVY...

YOU'RE IN SHOW BIZ — MAYBE YOU'VE HEARD THE EXPRESSION. "YOU AIN'T SEEN NOTHIN' YET —"

4

LOOK, BITCH — __BACK OFF__! __NOBODY__ PUSHES JIMMY PLUGG AROUND —

REALLY?

TAKE IT EASY, HONEY — OKAY, DAVE AND ME, WE DID SOME DEALING FOR HIS OLD MAN... SOME RUNS UP FROM MEXICO, BY BOAT MOSTLY — BUT IT WAS KID STUFF. I STILL DO A LITTLE DEALIN', OKAY?

WHAT ABOUT DAVE?

HE WAS GOIN' STRAIGHT — THAT GIRL OF HIS WOULDN'T HAVE IT ANY OTHER WAY! AND DAVE HAD THE BRAINS TO MAKE IT, ON THE SQUARE — HE WAS A BUSINESS GRAD, B-PLUS AVERAGE —

HEY, YOU WANT TO COME IN AND DO YOUR JOB, SHIT-FOR-BRAINS?

IS IT OKAY?

SURE — BUT KEEP IN MIND __NOBODY__ PUSHES JIMMY PLUGG AROUND...

AT POLICE HQ THAT AFTERNOON, I MET WITH SGT. VALER, AND CAPTAIN MEYERS OF THE B.C.I.

THIS IS THE SKETCH OUR ARTIST WORKED UP OF THE KILLER AS HE MIGHT LOOK WITHOUT BEARD AND CURLY HAIR —

IS THIS A COPY? CAN I MARK IT UP?

SURE.

THIS IS THE MAN WHO TRIED TO KILL ME IN THE ELEVATOR —

5

THE SAME MAN TRIED TO KILL YOU THE VERY NEXT DAY AFTER THE HONEYMOON KILLING...?

THAT'S INSANITY! WHY WOULD HE DO SUCH A THING?

YOU'RE SIMPLY A BYSTANDER — A WITNESS WHO SAW NOTHING EXCEPT A KILLER-IN-DISGUISE...

UNLESS HE'S IN THE HIRE OF DOMINIC MUERTA — WHO MIGHT FIGURE ME TO GET INVOLVED.

MEANING MUERTA HIRED HIS OWN NIECE'S DEATH? HARD TO BUY. STILL, THE GUN THE KILLER LEFT IN THE ELEVATOR WAS A PROFESSIONAL'S TOOL... MAYBE THIS IS A MOB-RELATED KILL...

A PRIVATE DETECTIVE CAN LOSE A LICENSE OVER WHAT I DID NEXT: I WITHELD THE ASKAM INFORMATION...

WELL, KEEP DIGGING, GENTS — YOU MAY COME UP WITH SOMETHING.

SEE TO IT YOU DON'T, MS. TREE. YOU'RE A WITNESS IN THIS, NOTHING MORE.

WE'LL NOTIFY YOU IF OUR NATIONAL CHECKS IDENTIFY THE HITMAN.

I SHOULD'VE TOLD THEM, OF COURSE — AND THEY'LL MAKE THE ASKAM CONNECTION THEMSELVES, SOON ENOUGH — BUT I WANTED TO RUN WITH IT, FOR A WHILE.

WHY ARE YOU TELLING ME ALL THIS, MS. TREE? SINCE WHEN DO YOU LET ME IN ON YOUR CRUSADES?

WE'VE GOT A PAYING CUSTOMER ON THIS ONE, DAN: FRANCESCO MUERTA. HOW WOULD YOU LIKE TO GO TO FLORIDA?

HOT DAMN!

6

I SPENT THE REST OF THE AFTERNOON ON THE PHONE, GETTING BACKGROUND INFORMATION FROM POLICE REPORTER J.M. AYDER OF THE MIAMI _HERALD_ —

THEN I CAUGHT UP WITH DAN, WHO WAS ALREADY AT THE AIRPORT —

J.M.'LL FILL YOU IN, IN DETAIL, AT THE _HERALD_; BUT HERE'S THE BASIC OUTLINE...

"THE ASKAM BROTHERS — JOHN 'THE FOX' AND ROBERT 'THE WOLF' ASKAM — WERE AMONG DOMINIC MUERTA'S TOP DOPE SUPPLIERS THROUGHOUT THE 'SIXTIES AND 'SEVENTIES."

"BUT THE ASKAMS GOT EMBROILED IN LOCAL POLITICAL SCANDALS, AROUND '76 —"

MAYORAL CANDIDATE WITHDRAWS

CAMPAIGN CONTRIBUTIONS FROM ASKAM "CRIME FAMILY" EXPOSED

"AND THEN A GANG WAR WITH THE EMERGING LATIN MOB FACTIONS CREATED, WELL... MUCHO BAD PUBLICITY."

AFTER WHICH, DOMINIC MUERTA APPARENTLY BROKE WITH THE ASKAMS — WHO HAVE DECLINED IN POWER ACCORDINGLY.

"LATEST DEVELOPMENT WAS LAST SUMMER, WHEN ROBERT ASKAM — DAVE'S UNCLE — WAS KILLED IN HIS OWN HOME. HOW THAT FITS IN, IF IT DOES, ISN'T KNOWN."

WHO DO YOU WANT ME TO TALK TO, MS. TREE?

ANYBODY IN THE ASKAM ORGANIZATION YOU CAN GET TO — JOHN ASKAM HIMSELF, IF YOU CAN PULL IT OFF.

OH, AND DAN — TRY NOT TO GET KILLED.

SEE WHAT I CAN DO BOSS —

7

WHEN I GOT HOME, AROUND SEVEN, THERE WAS A MESSAGE ON MY ANSWER MACHINE —

MICHAEL, THIS IS PATRICK — I'M IN TOWN, WRESTLING WITH MY PUBLISHER — STILL ON FOR TONIGHT?

PATRICK? MICHAEL. I SURE COULD USE A NIGHT OUT — BEATS OPENING UP A CAN OF SOUP AT HOME. OF COURSE I LIKE CHICAGO-STYLE PIZZA!

YOU KNOW WHAT I LIKE ABOUT TAKING YOU OUT TO DINNER?

NO, WHAT?

SINCE YOU'RE A PRIVATE EYE, AND I'M A MYSTERY WRITER, THIS IS RESEARCH — HENCE, DEDUCTABLE.

YOU KNOW, I DUG OUT ONE OF YOUR NOVELS FROM MY HUSBAND'S BOX OF PAPERBACKS.

HOPE IT WAS HITMAN #21 — THAT'S MY FINEST HOUR.

LOOK — ARE YOU DOING ALL RIGHT? I HOPE MY FLIP ATTITUDE DOESN'T SEEM CALLOUS, AFTER THAT... TRAGEDY AT PINE BEACH.

NOT AT ALL. YOU'RE JUST WHAT THE DOCTOR ORDERED.

"GOOD," PATRICK SAID. "NOW, WHY DON'T WE GO SEE WHAT'S PLAYING AT YOUR APARTMENT... "

Ms. TREE

"DEATH DO US PART"

by Max Collins and Terry Beatty

Chapter Six — MY COLD, DEAD FINGERS

© 1983 Max Collins and Terry Beatty

LOOK OUT!

SCREECH

DAMN.

WE BETTER CALL THE COPS.

FOR WHAT GOOD IT'LL DO.

SGT. VALER WAS THERE IN TEN MINUTES —

I SAW SOME LIGHT REFLECT OFF HIS GUN, OR I WOULDN'T'VE BEEN ABLE TO REACT IN TIME.

IT WAS A LATE MODEL BUICK. THERE WAS MUD SPATTERED ON THE LICENSE PLATE — COULDN'T GET THE NUMBER.

SOMEBODY WANTS YOU DEAD. LADY — CAN I MAKE A SUGGESTION?

CAN I STOP YOU?

TAKE A VACATION. GET AS FAR AWAY FROM THIS CITY — AND THIS CASE — AS HUMANLY POSSIBLE.

THANKS FOR SAVING MY LIFE.

CAN'T YOU THINK OF A BETTER WAY TO THANK ME?

2

YOU SEEM PREOCCUPIED.

GETTING SHOT AT CAN DO THAT TO YOU.

I'M AT A DEAD-END. THE INVESTIGATION'S GONE COLD —

THERE WAS NOTHING MORE I COULD DO TILL I HEARD BACK FROM DAN, IN MIAMI —

I THINK I CAN GET YOU IN TO SEE JOHN ASKAM.

THE HERALD DID AN EXPOSÉ ON THE ASKAM CRIME FAMILY, AWHILE BACK, AND I WAS THE GUY WHO INTERVIEWED JOHN. DESPITE BEING IN ENEMY CAMPS, WE HIT IT OFF...

"THE FOX" IS A CHARMING GUY... LET ME MAKE A CALL —

I'M HERE TO SEE MR. ASKAM.

HE'S EXPECTING YOU — GO ON IN.

DIDN'T EXPECT TO FIND ME AT WORK, DID YOU, MR. GREEN? I AM IN MOURNING FOR MY SON — BUT LIFE — AND BUSINESS — GOES ON.

DAVID AND I WERE NOT CLOSE, YOU SEE.

HAS THAT ALWAYS BEEN THE CASE? OR WAS IT JUST SINCE HE REJECTED GOING INTO THE FAMILY BUSINESS?

3

THAT WAS DAVID'S CHOICE — I WOULD'VE LIKED HIM TO FOLLOW IN MY FOOTSTEPS, BUT HE CHOSE NOT TO. I'M A LEGITIMATE BUSINESSMAN, MR. GREEN, WHETHER YOU CARE TO BELIEVE THAT OR NOT.

A LEGITIMATE BUSINESSMAN, LIKE YOUR BROTHER — WHO WAS MURDERED LAST SUMMER?

YOU'RE RATHER BRASH, AREN'T YOU, MR. GREEN? RATHER LIKE MY SON... GET OUT.

I BLEW THAT INTERVIEW. MY LADY BOSS'LL HAVE MY BUTT.

CAN I HAVE IT WHEN SHE'S THROUGH?

THANKS FOR SHOWING ME AROUND MIAMI.

MY PLEASURE. THANKS FOR NOT ASKING ME ANY QUESTIONS ABOUT MR. ASKAM.

IT'S NOT ASKAM I CARE ABOUT — IT'S HIS DEAD SON...

I SEE — ACTUALLY, I KNEW DAVE — INTIMATELY.

HE WAS A NICE GUY. GOT OUT OF THE FAMILY BUSINESS WHEN... WELL, I SHOULDN'T GO INTO THAT.

MAYBE YOU SHOULD. I'M TRYING TO FIND HIS KILLER. WOULDN'T YOU LIKE TO HELP?

4

ASKAM'S SECRETARY GAVE YOU ALL THIS INFORMATION? I DON'T KNOW IF I WANT TO HEAR HOW YOU GOT THIS OUT OF HER...

WELL, THAT STORY WOULD COST YOU EXTRA, MS. TREE...

"BUT WHAT I GOT IS WORTH EVERY CENT YOU PAY ME... STARTING WITH ASKAM TELLING HIS SON TO MARRY TERESA MUERTA — "

WHY WOULD HE DO THAT?

TO LAY THE GROUNDWORK FOR A NEW ALLIANCE WITH THE MUERTAS — VERY "OLD WORLD," HUH?

"SEEMS DAVE MET TERESA IN FT. LAUDERDALE — THEY HAD A LITTLE 'SPRING BREAK' FLING; WHEN DAVE'S FATHER GOT WIND, HE SUGGESTED — DEMANDED - DAVE CULTIVATE THE RELATIONSHIP."

SO THAT'S WHY DAVE LEFT COLLEGE IN MIAMI AND TRANSFERRED TO CITY COLLEGE HERE.

RIGHT! THAT'S WHERE TERESA MUERTA WAS GOING —

"BUT DAVE AND TERESA'S SPRING FLING BLOSSOMED INTO SOMETHING MORE — THEY FELL IN LOVE. REALLY FELL IN LOVE..."

5

SO DAVE'S FATHER GOT HIS WISH — HIS SON MARRIED INTO THE MUERTA FAMILY — ONLY WITH DAVE TURNING HIS BACK ON THE FAMILY BUSINESS, IT WAS A VERY EMPTY VICTORY. NICE.

I APPRECIATE YOU COMING TO ME WITH THE INFORMATION ABOUT THE ASKAM/MUERTA CONNECTION, MS. TREE — I JUST WISH YOU'D DONE IT SOONER.

WHY? WOULD IT HAVE DONE YOU SOME GOOD?

NOT REALLY. WE KNEW MOST OF IT.

YOU DID?

WE AREN'T REQUIRED TO KEEP PRIVATE EYES, UH... ABREAST OF OUR INVESTIGATION.

BUT WE'D HAVE GIVEN YOU SOME POLICE PROTECTION. THAT SECOND ATTEMPT ON YOUR LIFE MIGHT'VE LED TO THE CAPTURE OF THE HITMAN.

YOU GUYS ARE GENIUSES! IT TAKES TWO ATTEMPTS ON MY LIFE BEFORE YOU THINK TO OFFER POLICE PROTECTION? WHICH, BY THE WAY, YOU CAN STICK UP...

OF COURSE IF YOU DON'T WANT TO HEAR WHAT ELSE WE KNOW ABOUT DAVE ASKAM AND HIS WIFE, THAT'S YOUR BUSINESS...

SPILL.

WE DON'T HAVE MUCH — JUST THAT ASKAM AND HIS BRIDE WERE BOTH GOING TO TESTIFY.

TESTIFY? WHERE? ON WHAT?

TO THE GRAND JURY IN MIAMI.

6

"IT SEEMS," MEYERS SAID, "THAT THE NIGHT ROBERT THE WOLF WAS MURDERED AT HOME, IN HIS BED..."

"HIS NEPHEW AND HIS GIRL WERE SLEEPING OVER... DAVE'S FATHER WAS TOO CONSERVATIVE TO PROVIDE THE COUPLE COHABITIVE QUARTERS, BUT DAVE'S UNCLE WASN'T..."

"THE COUPLE SAW THE HITMAN LEAVING... GOT A VERY GOOD LOOK AT HIM —"

THAT MUST HAVE BEEN THE POINT WHEN DAVE TOLD HER EVERYTHING... WHEN THEY DECIDED THEIR LOVE WAS STRONGER THAN THE CRIMINAL TIES THAT ALSO BOUND THEM...

YOU'RE RIGHT, MS. TREE. AND TERESA MUERTA HAD WITNESSED SOME SHADY DEALINGS, TOO, OVER THE YEARS.

SHE WAS NEGOTIATING TESTIFYING IN THIS CITY, WITH OUR D.A.'S OFFICE.

OUR D.A.'S OFFICE! UNTIL I SPLIT IT OPEN BY NAILING CHICK STEELE, THAT OFFICE WAS MUERTA-CONTROLLED!

RIGHT. BY THE WAY, HERE'S SOMETHING THE MIAMI P.D. TELEXED TO US: THE DRAWING THEIR POLICE ARTIST CAME UP WITH BASED ON THE COUPLE'S DESCRIPTION OF THE UNCLE'S MURDERER.

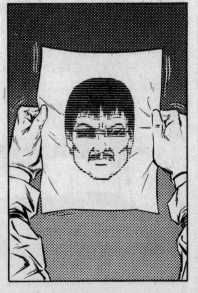

I WAS STILL TRYING TO DIGEST IT ALL WHEN I GOT BACK TO MY APARTMENT; THE ANSWER MACHINE WAS TAKING CARE OF AN INCOMING CALL...

THIS IS MICHAEL TREE... I CAN'T COME TO THE PHONE RIGHT NOW...

7

I WAS TOO TIRED TO PICK UP THE PHONE AND TELL WHOEVER IT WAS I WAS HOME...

MS. TREE. I AM SORRY TO HAVE MISSED YOU.

THIS IS DOMINIC MUERTA...

I'M HERE! WHAT IS IT?

WE'VE NOT MET, MS. TREE. BUT I FEEL I KNOW YOU. I WANT YOU TO KNOW I AM IN NO WAY RESPONSIBLE FOR MY NIECE'S DEATH.

SHE WAS A DISTURBED GIRL. I MERELY ENCOURAGED HER TO SEEK HELP. —CLICK—

MUERTA? MUERTA?

I'M GLAD YOU AGREED TO "GET AWAY FROM IT ALL" FOR THE WEEKEND — YOU'LL LIKE MY LITTLE HIDEAWAY.

I'M SURE I WILL. I NEED SOME PEACE AND QUIET, TO THINK. HEY! LOOK AT THAT BUMPER STICKER...

"CRAZY RIGHT-WING NUT," I SAID. "HUSH!" PATRICK SAID. "THAT'S PROBABLY ONE OF MY READERS."

I'LL GIVE UP MY GUN WHEN THEY PRY IT FROM MY COLD, DEAD FINGERS

I DIDN'T GET A LOOK AT THE GUY AS PATRICK WENT QUICKLY AROUND HIM...

8

Ms. TREE

"DEATH DO US PART"
by Max Collins and Terry Beatty

Chapter Seven

IN THE FINAL ANALYSIS

PATRICK AND I ARRIVED AT HIS LAKE HOME AROUND DUSK, DR. KASSEL...

WHAT D'YOU THINK OF MY LITTLE WRITER'S HIDEAWAY?

BLOOD 'N' GUTS MUST PAY PRETTY WELL...

© 1983 Max Collins and Terry Beatty

THE HITMAN SERIES MAY NOT BE ART, BUT IT KEEPS THE LIGHTS ON IN THIS JOINT...

CLIK

I DID READ ONE OF YOUR BOOKS, LAST NIGHT...

OH, REALLY? WHICH ONE?

HITMAN #21 — YOUR FINEST HOUR, YOU CALLED IT. DO HITMEN REALLY WORK IN PAIRS, LIKE THEY DO IN YOUR STORIES?

1

I WOULDN'T HAVE THE SLIGHTEST IDEA.

WELL, IT WOULD MAKE SENSE — A BACK-UP MAN TO STAKE OUT THE VICTIM, DO THE GROUNDWORK; AND THE TRIGGERMAN HIMSELF.

D'YOU SUPPOSE YOUR "ADMIRER" WITH THE VARIOUS COLOR HAIR WORKS WITH SOMEBODY?

IF SO, I NEVER SAW HIM... OR HER. BUT YOUR NOVEL GAVE ME A HUNCH.

REALLY?

YES — QUITE A PLOT TWIST, THERE — A RESORT BEING USED BY THE MOB TO ARRANGE KEY DEATHS —

I'D FORGOTTEN ABOUT THAT... I'VE DONE 40 OF THOSE PULP THINGS, Y'KNOW.

SLICK PREMISE: THE MOB SENDS ONE OF THEIR OWN — WHOSE NERVOUS PROBLEMS MAKE SAID PERSON UNRELIABLE — TO A CERTAIN RESORT.

THEN THE HITMEN CREATE AN "ACCIDENTAL DEATH"; IT'S COMING BACK TO ME.

THOUGHT IT MIGHT.

COULD I USE YOUR PHONE FOR A MOMENT, PATRICK? IT'S A LONG DISTANCE CALL, IN THE CITY...

I GOT A ROYALTY CHECK THIS WEEK. GO AHEAD — SPLURGE.

2

CAPTAIN MEYERS? DID MY HUNCH PAY OFF?

APPARENTLY, YES, MS. TREE – THERE HAVE BEEN THREE "ACCIDENTAL" DEATHS OVER THE PAST TWO YEARS AT PINE BEACH... ALL INVOLVING PEOPLE AT LEAST PERIPHERALLY MUERTA-INVOLVED.

WHY DIDN'T YOU PICK UP ON THIS SOONER?

"THE MEN INVOLVED IN THESE SEEMING ACCIDENTS WERE NOT HOODS, MS. TREE – BUT LEGIT BUSINESSMEN WHO MAY HAVE BEEN MOB-CONNECTED."

WE'LL HAVE TO INVESTIGATE FURTHER TO MAKE ANYTHING SUBSTANTIAL OF THIS –

WHY DON'T YOU DO THAT?

WHEELS OF JUSTICE GRINDING SLOWLY?

WHO SAYS THE POLICE AND JUSTICE HAVE ANYTHING TO DO WITH EACH OTHER?

HEY, YOU'RE SUPPOSED TO BE HERE TO RELAX; FORGET BUSINESS. HOW 'BOUT A MOONLIGHT SWIM?

GO ON DOWN TO THE BEACH AND SEE HOW THE WATER AGREES WITH YOU... I'M GOING TO PUT SOME BEER AND SANDWICHES IN A PICNIC BASKET.

MICHAEL?

YES?

NOTHING. LOVE YA, THAT'S ALL. SEE YOU IN A MINUTE.

3

IT WAS VERY MUCH LIKE THE WOODS NEAR PINE BEACH, DR. KASSEL — THERE WAS A BALMY BREEZE, A WHISPER OF WIND AS GENTLE AS A KISS — THE WORLD BATHED IN MOONLIGHT —

I STOOD ON THE BEACH, WAITING... WAITING FOR THE SLIGHTEST SOUND — LIKE A TWIG BEING SNAPPED UNDERFOOT...

CRACK!

WELL. IT'S ABOUT TIME WE MET; I FEEL AS THOUGH I KNOW YOU.

ENJOY THE MOMENT WHILE IT LASTS, BITCH.

BLAM

OH, I AM.

THE BREEZE TURNED CHILL, SUDDENLY. NOTHING LEFT TO DO BUT. WAIT... WAIT FOR THE REAL KILLER.

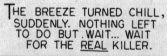

4

HELLO, PATRICK. FORGET YOUR PICNIC BASKET?

MICHAEL — WHAT — WHAT THE HELL HAPPENED, HERE? I HEARD A SHOT —

DIDN'T EXPECT THAT, DID YOU? THOUGHT YOUR PARTNER'D USE A SILENCED GUN, RIGHT? WELL, IT WAS MY GUN YOU HEARD...

MY... PARTNER?

YES. YOU'RE HIS BACK-UP MAN, AFTER ALL.

THERE WERE THREE CABINS AT PINE BEACH — YOUR PARTNER'S, THE VICTIMS' — AND MINE.

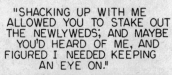

"SHACKING UP WITH ME ALLOWED YOU TO STAKE OUT THE NEWLYWEDS; AND MAYBE YOU'D HEARD OF ME, AND FIGURED I NEEDED KEEPING AN EYE ON."

YOU'VE SEEN TOO MANY BAD MOVIES, MICHAEL.

I DON'T GO TO THE MOVIES, MUCH... BUT I READ.

"I READ YOUR BOOK, PATRICK — YOU SMUGLY CALLED MY ATTENTION TO IT — THE STORY OF A PAIR OF HITMEN WHO CREATED 'ACCIDENTS' AT A PINE BEACH—LIKE RESORT."

HITMAN
by DEREK RODD
No.21
The Shrinking Violent

YOU'RE CRAZY. MICHAEL! THAT'S PURE COINCIDENCE —

NOTHING ABOUT YOU IS "PURE," PATRICK. INCLUDING YOU SAVING MY LIFE YESTERDAY —

5

"THAT WAS A CONVENIENT WAY FOR YOU TO GET FURTHER INTO MY CONFIDENCE — YOU WERE ALREADY IN MY PANTS, AFTER ALL. SHORTLY AFTER, YOU INVITED ME HERE — "

WHERE THIS PIECE OF MEAT WAS SUPPOSED TO KILL ME. RIGHT?

YOU'RE SICK, MICHAEL! PSYCHOTIC!

WHAT WERE YOU DOING AT PINE BEACH, PATRICK? SEEKING RELAXATION, TRYING TO WRITE, YOU SAID...

"YET YOU LIVE IN AN ISOLATED HIDEAWAY ON A LAKE — PROVIDING THE SAME SORT OF SECLUSION AND SOLITUDE AS PINE BEACH."

SO WHY GO TO PINE BEACH, PATRICK? EXCEPT TO PLY YOUR OTHER TRADE...

YOU'RE WRONG! YOU'RE DELUDED — YOU'RE CONFUSING ME WITH YOUR OTHER LOVER — CHICK STEELE, WHO BETRAYED YOU!

IT'S YOUR SICKNESS THAT'S CREATED THIS PARANOID CONSTRUCT, THIS WEB OF MEANINGLESS COINCIDENCE!

I COULD NEVER KILL ANYONE, MICHAEL — YOU SAW ME THAT NIGHT... I... I GOT SICK. DID I FAKE THAT?

6

MS. TREE - THE COLD, CRAZY BITCH IN A TRENCHCOAT. IT'S ALL A POSE, ISN'T IT? ALL IT TOOK WAS MY BOYISH CHARM TO WEAKEN YOU FOR A MOMENT, AND A MOMENT CAN BE A LIFETIME...

KA-BLAM!

ARRGGHHH—

NO OFFENSE MEANT TO YOUR BOYISH CHARM, PATRICK - BUT I LET YOU TAKE THAT GUN. I PLUGGED THE BARREL WITH SAND.

KILL ME...

I ALREADY HAVE. YOU'LL BLEED TO DEATH, PATRICK. BUT YOU'LL PASS OUT SOON. IT WON'T BE A SLOW DEATH... OTHERWISE I'D PUT YOU OUT OF YOUR MISERY. I'M NOT UNFEELING.

I TOLD CAPTAIN MEYERS I WASN'T EVEN PRESENT DURING THE SHOOTING — THAT I HEARD SHOTS FROM THE HOUSE AND FOUND THEM BOTH DEAD.

THESE TRAUMATIC EXPERIENCES EXPLAIN THE NEW ELEMENTS IN YOUR RECCURING DREAM, DO THEY NOT?

"THE MAN ON THE BEACH WHO APPROACHES YOU — OBVIOUSLY THIS REPRESENTS PATRICK."

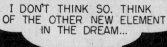

I DON'T THINK SO. THINK OF THE OTHER NEW ELEMENT IN THE DREAM...

"THE SAND CASTLE THE CHILD IS BUILDING - MY SUBCONSCIOUS KNOWS WHO THE KILLER IS, DOCTOR. AND SO DO I."

YOU. YOU'RE THE KILLER.

"DOMINIC MUERTA HIMSELF TOLD ME... HE ADVISED HIS TROUBLED NIECE TO 'SEEK HELP' — AND SHE CAME TO YOU: THE 'COMPANY' PSYCHIATRIST."

AND YOU SENT HER TO PINE BEACH RESORT, WHERE YOU GET KICK-BACKS FOR REFERRING PATIENTS... LIKE ME. UNLUCKY ACCIDENT FOR YOU THAT I HAPPENED TO GO AT THE SAME TIME AS THE HONEYMOONING KIDS.

YOU'RE MUERTA'S HANDPICKED SHRINK, AREN'T YOU, DR. KASSEL? HE SENDS BAD RISKS TO YOU, POOR SOULS WHO DON'T REALIZE YOU'RE A DOCTOR WHO MIGHT PRESCRIBE A PAIR OF HITMEN.

"BUT THIS WASN'T A MUERTA HIT; HIS HITS HAD BEEN STAGED AS ACCIDENTS. THIS WAS ANOTHER KIND OF HIT: THOSE KIDS HAD SEEN THE HITMAN WHO KILLED ASKAM, AND WERE PLANNING TO 'TESTIFY — "

WHO HIRED THEM TO KILL ASKAM? MUERTA? OH, WELL. IT DOESN'T MATTER.

YOU HAD THOSE KIDS KILLED. TO KEEP THEM FROM TESTIFYING. TO KEEP THE THREAD FROM LEADING TO YOU.

DOCTOR/PATIENT CONFERENCE
DO NOT DISTURB

KA-BLAM

CALL THE POLICE, WOULD YOU? AND I'D LIKE TO SETTLE UP MY BILL, WHILE I'M HERE...

8

FOR JOHNNY CRAIG

RED LIGHT

From the Files of Ms. Tree...
RED LIGHT

by Max Allan Collins

I was stopped at a light, on my way home from working late at the office, when the guy climbed in on the rider's side and pointed his gun at me.

It wasn't much of a gun, but then he wasn't much of a guy: he was chocolate-black and had Michael Jackson's curls and approximate weight and a similar plastic beauty. Only I didn't figure him for a rock star, or a Jehovah's Witness, either.

"You oughta keep your doors locked, babe," he said, flashing his caps. It was a dazzling smile, I had to give him that much; but it was a nervous smile. And there was blood spattered on his blue satin shirt and skinny white leather tie; also on one satin sleeve there was a tear, or rather a slash, just below the bicep, and a circle of red dampness grew around it. His white leather pants were spotless, however.

"Cut yourself shaving?" I asked.

His smile faded and only the nervousness remained. "You're a pretty cool customer, babe, that much I got to hand you."

"The meter's running," I said. "Where to?"

He was looking back over his shoulder. "Take a left when the light changes, then cut through the alley and double back to Wells."

Red turned to green, and I did what he said.

He smiled smugly as he continued looking back over his shoulder. "Think we lost 'em. Just keep driving. You know where the Skyview Hotel is?"

"Out by the airport?"

"You got it."

"That where we're going?"

"That's where we're goin', babe."

I got on the expressway; it was well after rush hour - lights blinked nervously in the night, though not as nervously as my passenger with the gun. For a skinny little

illustrations by Terry Beatty

man who obviously fancied himself cool, my main man here was a beat away from coming apart at the seams.

"How long have you been a pimp?" I asked him.

He shot me a narrow-eyed look that was at once angry and frightened. "Just drive, bitch," he said.

"Hey, and here I thought I was your 'babe.'"

He studied me; the gun in his hand - a nickel-plated .32 with a pearl-handle - studied me, too. "Ain't I seen you someplace before?"

"That's a pretty smooth line," I said, smiling over at him. "Is that how you reel in the little girls from Michigan when you pick 'em up at the bus station?"

"Shut-up," he said. There was almost a pout in his voice. He was beginning to think he'd climbed in the wrong car.

He was right.

"Anybody following us?" I asked.

He was looking behind him again. "Not that I can see. But step on it. Just don't attract any sirens."

I shrugged. "I go sixty-five along here all the time. Never been picked up yet."

"Do it, then!" He almost spit the words.

"Nice teeth you got there. How much they cost you?"

He puts the gun in my neck. Leaned into me. He smelled good. "You're a nice-looking piece of work, but you got a smart-ass mouth. And I don't like that in my ladies."

"No offense. I'm just...nervous. It's not every day a guy jumps in my car and holds a gun on me."

"You ain't nervous enough, far as I'm concerned."

"We all show our nervousness in different ways, to different degrees. With me, it comes out in wisecracks. Now, you, you don't seem nervous at all."

That was a lie, of course, but it was also sort of a compliment. It isn't true that you can't bullshit a bullshitter, you know.

"But I wouldn't blame you if you **were** nervous," I said. "A situation like this, who wouldn't be?"

He let air out. Pulled the gun away from my neck. Slid back over by his window.

"Well, I'm not, he said, wincing as he flexed the bleeding arm. "Nervous."

"It's five minutes to the airport. Care if I smoke?"

"Light up. Die of cancer. See if I give a shit."

I punched in the lighter; a few seconds later it popped out of the dash. I pulled it out and pressed it to the hand holding the gun. Skin sizzled, he screamed, shot himself in the leg, and I slammed on the brakes.

The windshield didn't shatter, when his head slammed into it, but it made a lovely lace-like effect, as if the most artistic spider in the world had had a hand in it. And here my passenger had managed it all with a simple nod of the head.

I ended up my sliding skid along the roadside. Other cars glided by in the cool night, not noticing us, or not caring, as I hopped out and went around on the driver's side and pulled him out onto the shoulder. There was blood in his pretty curls, but he wasn't dead. I had my gloves on, so picking up the little gun he'd dropped in my car was no problem. I gave him a nudge or two with my foot and he rolled down the embankment into the ditch. Then I went back to the car, got my own gun out of my purse and went down to see how my main man was doing.

He was on his back, just beginning to rouse. He pushed up on one elbow, touched his bloody head, look up groggily.

"Who...who the fuck are you, anyway?" he managed.

I removed the clip from his automatic; emptied the bullets in one cupped hand, tossed them into the night. Put the clip back, tossed it in his lap. Then I bent over and, holding my gun on him, edged a money clip from out his tight white pants. I peeled off a hundred, tossed the clip back at him.

"That's for my windshield," I said. "And my name's Michael Tree."

"Oh, shit...."

"You might've seen my picture in the paper. Every now and then I kill somebody I don't like."

"I didn't do anything to you..."

"Not enough to kill you over." I turned away. "I'll see you around."

From behind me his voice was a razor cutting the night.

"You're one cold bitch, ain't you?"

I didn't turn when I spoke. "That coming from a pimp I take as high praise indeed."

I started up the embankment.

A red Cadillac came careening up, and three women jumped out, almost simultaneously: a redhead, a blonde, a brunette. All of them had spandex pants on and various skimpy, spanglely tops. All of them wore expressions so intensely angry the make-up on their pretty faces was cracking.

The redhead had a knife in her hand and the blade was bloody.

"We saw him get in your car waving his gun," she said breathlessly. "Figured he made you drive him."

"You figured right," I said.

The brunette said, "We thought we lost you, but then we figured he might head back to the Skyview so we got on the expressway and..."

The redhead cut in, nodded toward my car. "What happened?"

"That's my line," I said.

"He killed Candy," the blonde said. She was maybe twenty and had a face harder than the gun in my hand.

"He said she was holding out on him," the brunette said, her mouth a thin red line, her eyes full of water, "and he shot her!"

The redhead said, "And I took this out of my bag and cut him! Then he ran..."

"Can't blame him," I said.

"Where is he?" the redhead with the knife demanded.

I pointed down the embankment. "Down there. Waiting for you."

And I drove off and left them to it.

The monthly MS. TREE comic book is available by first class subscription. Send check or money order for $33 (US) or $40 (Cdn) to AARDVARK VANAHEIM INC. Box 1674 Station "C" Kitchener, Ontario Canada N2G 4R2.